C000278430

CONTENTS

ZOOOOOOM!!!!

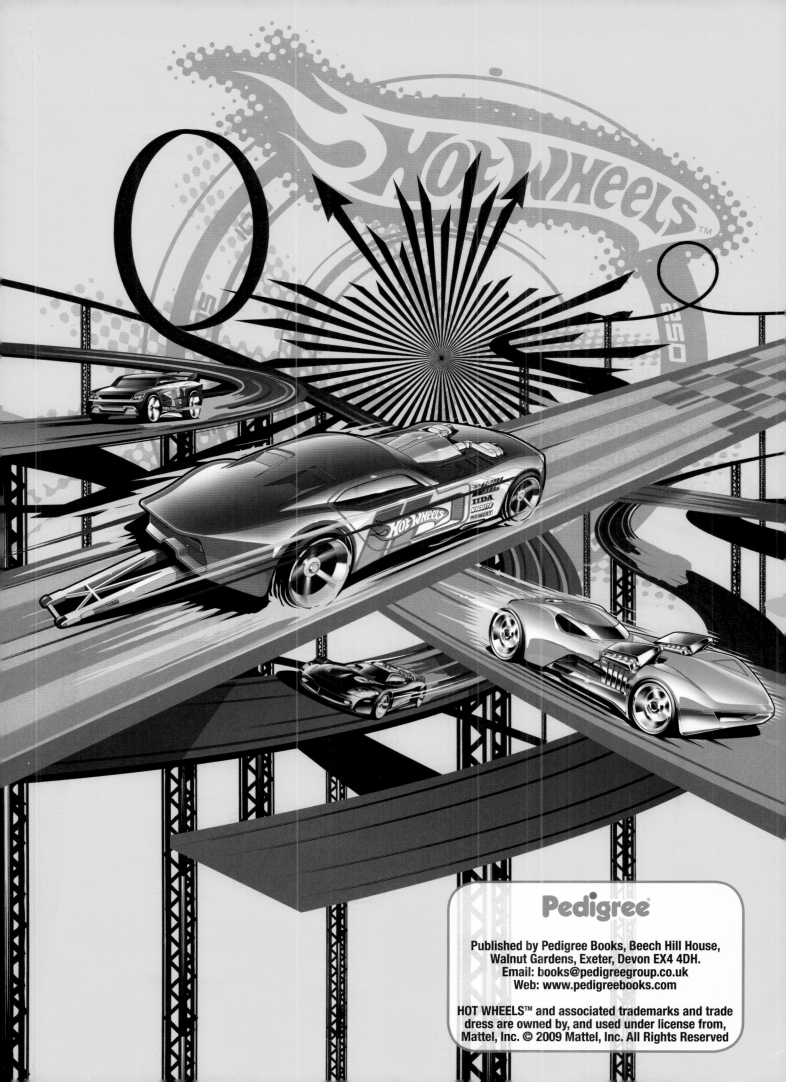

Pedigree®

Published by Pedigree Books, Beech Hill House,
Walnut Gardens, Exeter, Devon EX4 4DH.
Email: books@pedigreegroup.co.uk
Web: www.pedigreebooks.com

HOT WHEELS™ and associated trademarks and trade
dress are owned by, and used under license from,
Mattel, Inc. © 2009 Mattel, Inc. All Rights Reserved

GET BEHIND THE WHEEL!

EVERY HOT WHEELS DRIVER
NEEDS A DRIVING LICENCE
BEFORE THEY JUMP BEHIND
THE WHEEL OF THEIR
FAVOURITE MOTOR. FILL IN
YOUR DETAILS BELOW,
THEN ADD A PHOTOGRAPH
OF YOURSELF TO COMPLETE
YOUR DRIVER'S LICENCE.

HOT WHEELS

DRIVER'S LICENCE

INSERT
PHOTO
HERE

NAME:

ADDRESS:

DATE OF BIRTH:

CAR'S NAME:

CAR'S COLOUR:

KNOW YOUR HOT WHEELS MOTORS!

NITRO DOORSLAMMER

TOP SPEED:	190MPH
0 – 60MPH:	5.8 SECS
ENGINE:	V8
POWER:	375 BHP

CIRCLE TRACKER

TOP SPEED:	175MPH
0 – 60MPH:	4.6 SECS
ENGINE:	V6
POWER:	356 BHP

BASSLINE

TOP SPEED:	217MPH
0 – 60MPH:	3.6 SECS
ENGINE:	V10
POWER:	500 BHP

ROCKET BOX

TOP SPEED:	160MPH
0 – 60MPH:	3.4 SECS
ENGINE:	V6
POWER:	650 BHP

PROTOTYPE H24

TOP SPEED:	210MPH
0 – 60MPH:	3.9 SECS
ENGINE:	V12
POWER:	615 BHP

SPINE BUSTER

TOP SPEED:	204MPH
0 – 60MPH:	3.5 SECS
ENGINE:	V10
POWER:	450 BHP

TWIN MILL

TOP SPEED:	195MPH
0 – 60MPH:	3.2 SECS
ENGINE:	V8
POWER:	650 BHP

BONE SHAKER

TOP SPEED:	197MPH
0 – 60MPH:	3.2 SECS
ENGINE:	V10
POWER:	627 BHP

HOLLOW BACK

TOP SPEED:	203MPH
0 – 60MPH:	4.4 SECS
ENGINE:	V12
POWER:	505 BHP

KNOW YOUR HOT WHEELS MOTORS!

SUZUKA

TOP SPEED:	199MPH
0 – 60MPH:	3.8 SECS
ENGINE:	V12
POWER:	505 BHP

MERCY BREAKER

TOP SPEED:	212MPH
0 – 60MPH:	4.1 SECS
ENGINE:	V10
POWER:	626 BHP

SURF CRATE

TOP SPEED:	217MPH
0 – 60MPH:	3.7 SECS
ENGINE:	V10
POWER:	570 BHP

FAT FISH

TOP SPEED:	180MPH
0 – 60MPH:	4.5 SECS
ENGINE:	V8
POWER:	360 BHP

RIVITED

TOP SPEED:	200MPH
0 – 60MPH:	4.3 SECS
ENGINE:	V6
POWER:	444 BHP

RODGER DODGER

TOP SPEED:	207MPH
0 – 60MPH:	3.1 SECS
ENGINE:	V12
POWER:	665 BHP

HARD DRIVE

TOP SPEED:	211MPH
0 – 60MPH:	4.4 SECS
ENGINE:	V6
POWER:	540 BHP

URBAN AGENT

TOP SPEED:	203MPH
0 – 60MPH:	3.8 SECS
ENGINE:	V8
POWER:	346 BHP

JACK HAMMER

TOP SPEED:	198MPH
0 – 60MPH:	3.9 SECS
ENGINE:	V8
POWER:	523 BHP

COOL ONE

TOP SPEED:	206MPH
0 – 60MPH:	4.3 SECS
ENGINE:	V12
POWER:	445 BHP

SOOO FAST

TOP SPEED:	186MPH
0 – 60MPH:	4.2 SECS
ENGINE:	V8
POWER:	370 BHP

DRAGSTER

TOP SPEED:	198MPH
0 – 60MPH:	4.2 SECS
ENGINE:	V8
POWER:	438 BHP

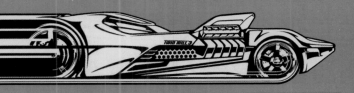

DEORA

TOP SPEED:	222MPH
0 – 60MPH:	3.2 SECS
ENGINE:	V6
POWER:	479 BHP

24 SEVEN

TOP SPEED:	185MPH
0 – 60MPH:	3.9 SECS
ENGINE:	V10
POWER:	623 BHP

PURPLE PASSION

TOP SPEED:	195MPH
0 – 60MPH:	3.4 SECS
ENGINE:	V12
POWER:	645 BHP

BULLY GOAT

TOP SPEED:	203MPH
0 – 60MPH:	4.5 SECS
ENGINE:	V6
POWER:	510 BHP

ULTRA RAGE

TOP SPEED:	218MPH
0 – 60MPH:	4.8 SECS
ENGINE:	V10
POWER:	310 BHP

RAT BOMB

TOP SPEED:	210MPH
0 – 60MPH:	3.2 SECS
ENGINE:	V8
POWER:	359 BHP

MED EVIL

TOP SPEED:	216MPH
0 – 60MPH:	3.4 SECS
ENGINE:	V8
POWER:	415 BHP

OVER BOARD 454

TOP SPEED:	198MPH
0 – 60MPH:	4.6 SECS
ENGINE:	V12
POWER:	550 BHP

PARADOX

TOP SPEED:	210MPH
0 – 60MPH:	3.2 SECS
ENGINE:	V12
POWER:	440 BHP

JET THREAT

TOP SPEED:	178MPH
0 – 60MPH:	4.1 SECS
ENGINE:	V6
POWER:	511 BHP

ZOTIC

TOP SPEED:	209MPH
0 – 60MPH:	3.5 SECS
ENGINE:	V10
POWER:	356 BHP

ROCKET FIRE

TOP SPEED:	204MPH
0 – 60MPH:	3.7 SECS
ENGINE:	V8
POWER:	411 BHP

BURNIN' RUBBER!

HOT W...

THE HOT WHEELS MACHINES
ARE ALWAYS UP FOR A
RACE TO PROVE THEIR
SPEED AND POWER! LOOK
CAREFULLY AT THIS
PICTURE THEN ANSWER THE
QUESTIONS BELOW.

I. HOW MANY HOT WHEELS CARS ARE RACING?

FIVE,

2. WHAT IS THE NAME OF THE RACE?

Hot wheels winter race.

3. WHAT COLOUR IS THE CAR IN LAST PLACE?

RED

4. WHAT IS THE NAME OF THE HOT WHEELS CAR THAT HAS COME FIRST?

Hard drive

5. HOW MANY TYRES CAN YOU SEE IN THE PIT LANE?

twelve

6. HOW MANY CHEQUERED FLAGS CAN YOU SPOT ON THE PAGE?

seven

PARADIGM SHIFT PICK UP

PARADIGM SHIFT IS ON THE WAY TO COLLECT SOME PASSENGERS.

CAN YOU HELP HIS DRIVER MAKE IT THROUGH THE CITY STREETS TO REACH THEM?

START

FINISH

MISSING

HOT WHEELS™

THIS IS ONE CLOSE HOT WHEELS RACE! THE CARS HAVE BEEN NECK-AND-NECK ALL THE WAY, BUT NOW THEY'RE NEAR THE FINISH LINE, ONE'S BEEN CALLED IN FOR AN EMERGENCY PIT-STOP! LOOK WHICH CARS STARTED THE RACE AND THEN AT THOSE APPROACHING THE FINISH LINE. WHICH CAR IS MISSING? CHECK YOUR ANSWER AT THE BACK OF THE BOOK.

SUZUKA	FAT FISH	URBAN AGENT	5000 FAST	24 SEVEN

OVER BOARD 454	ZOTIC	ROCKET FIRE	CIRCLE TRACKER	NITRO DOORSLAMMER

THE MISSING CAR IS?

Suzuka??????

13

SPEEDY SHADOWS!

THESE HOT WHEELS MOTORS ARE WHIZZING AND SPEEDING AROUND, SHOWING OFF THEIR SHAPES! CHECK OUT THE SHADOWS BELOW, THEN SEE IF YOU CAN MATCH THEM TO THE CARS ON THE OPPOSITE PAGE. WRITE THE CORRECT NUMBER IN THE BOX WHEN YOU KNOW.

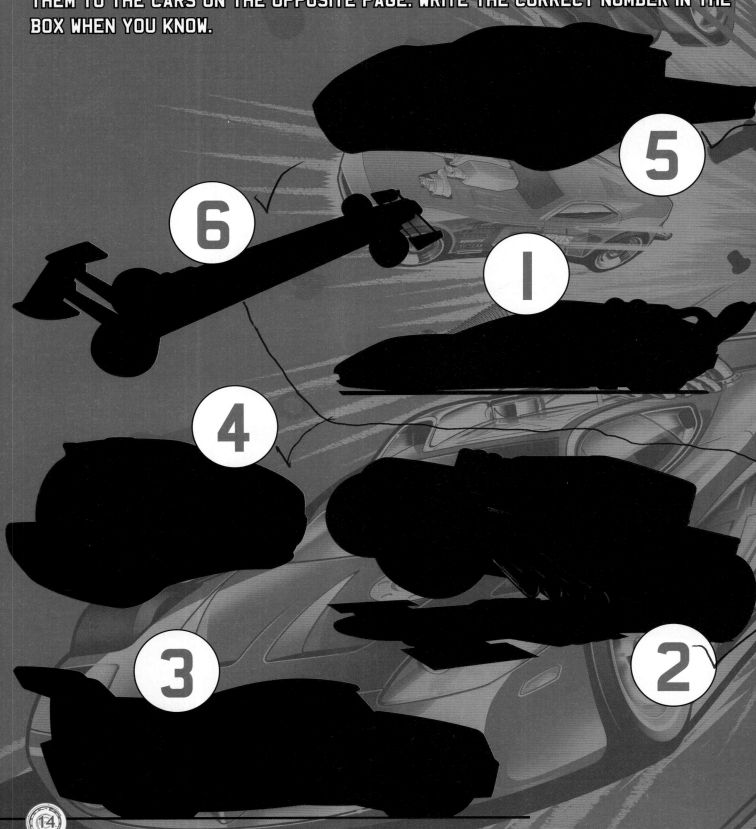

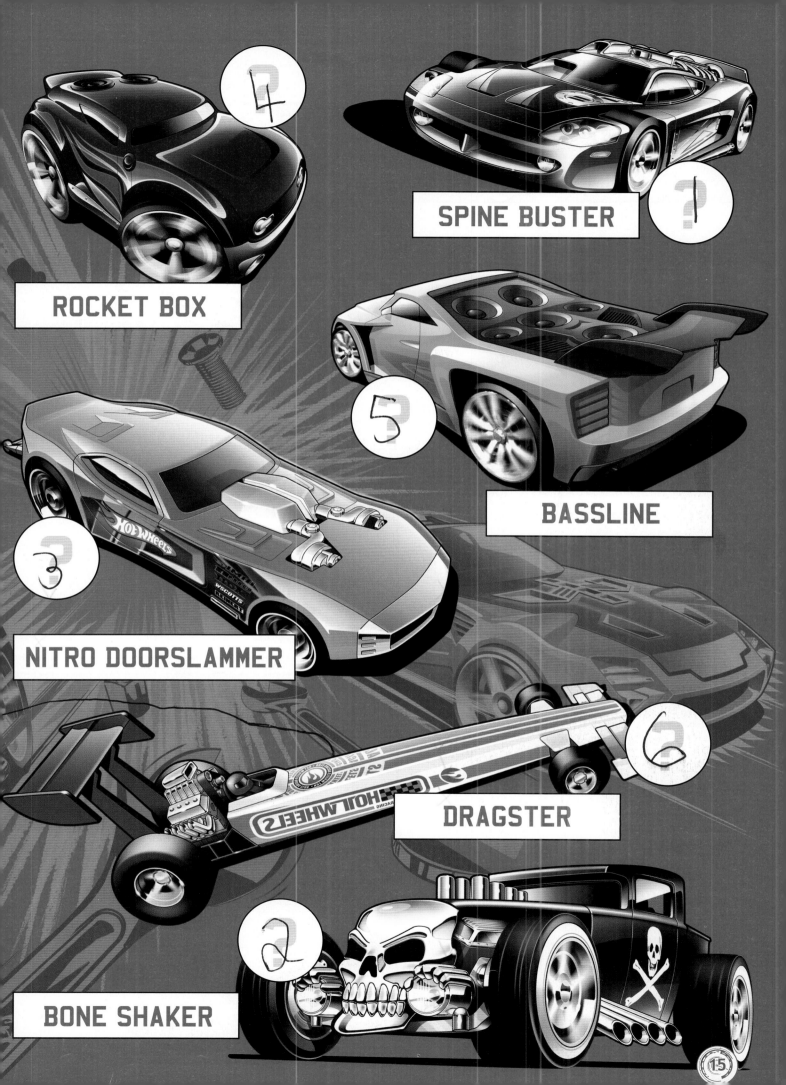

ROCKET BOX

SPINE BUSTER

BASSLINE

NITRO DOORSLAMMER

DRAGSTER

BONE SHAKER

15

HOT WHEELS QUIZ!

ARE YOU A HOT WHEELS BRAINBOX? DO YOU KNOW ALL THERE IS TO KNOW ABOUT CARS? TAKE THIS FUN QUIZ TO PROVE IT!

1. WHICH OF THESE CAN BE USED TO STOP A CAR?
    A HANDBRAKE ✓
    B INDICATOR ✗
    C ACCELERATOR ✗

2. WHERE DOES A VEHICLE STOP DURING A RACE TO REFUEL OR CHANGE TYRES?
    A REST STOP ✗
    B PIT STOP ✓
    C RACE STOP ✗

3. DURING A RACE, THE VEHICLES ARE WAVED OVER THE FINISH LINE BY A CHEQUERED FLAG. USUALLY, WHAT COLOUR IS THIS FLAG?
    A BLACK AND WHITE ✓
    B BLACK AND RED ✗
    C BLACK AND BLUE ✗

4. WHICH OF THESE IS THE NAME OF A PIECE OF METAL WHICH COVERS A WHEEL?
    A HUBCAP ✓
    B WHEEL HAT ✗
    C TYRE TOP ✗

5. WHERE WAS THE FIRST CAR TO RUN ON PETROL INVENTED?
    A FRANCE ✗
    B USA ✗
    C GERMANY ✓

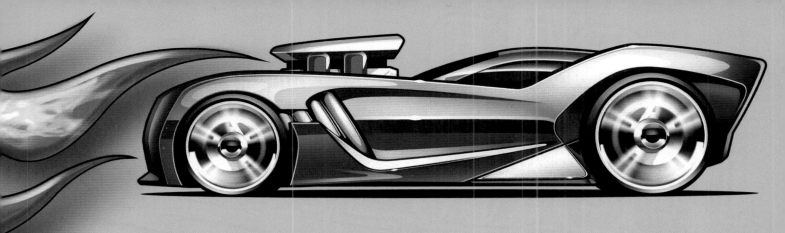

6. WHICH ENGINE PART FUNCTIONS LIKE A CHIMNEY?
A CARBURETTOR ☒
B EXHAUST PIPE ☑
C CYLINDER ☒

7. WHICH PEDAL WOULD YOU USE TO CHANGE GEAR?
A BRAKE ☒
B CLUTCH ☑
C ACCELERATOR ☒

8. THE NITRO DOORSLAMMER HAS 375BHP. WHAT DOES BHP STAND FOR?
A BURNING HOT POWER ☒
B BIG HORSE POWER ☒
C BRAKE HORSE POWER ☑

9. FAST FISH CAN REACH SPEEDS OF UP TO 180MPH. WHAT DOES MPH STAND FOR?
A MILES PER HOUR ☑
B MOTORING PER HOUR ☐
C MINUTES PER HOUR ☐

10. WHAT DOES THIS ROAD SIGN MEAN?

A PEDESTRIAN CROSSING ☐
B GIVE WAY ☐
C NO ENTRY ☑

SO, NOW YOU'VE SKIDDED TO A HALT, HOW DID YOU DO? CHECK YOUR ANSWERS AT THE BACK OF THE BOOK, THEN FIND YOUR PLACE ON THE WINNER'S PODIUM BELOW.

7 – 10 FIRST PLACE. CONGRATULATIONS! YOU'RE A TRUE CHAMPION!
4 – 6 SECOND PLACE. YOU DID WELL, BUT WERE PIPPED TO THE POST.
0 – 3 FINAL PLACE. DID YOUR FOOT SLIP OFF THE ACCELERATOR? YOU CAME IN LAST!

CAR JOURNEY FUN!

CAR JOURNEYS WILL ALWAYS BE COOL WITH THESE GREAT GAMES TO HELP PASS THE TIME. JUST DON'T DISTRACT THE DRIVER!

ALPHABET CHALLENGE

FIRST OF ALL, YOU NEED TO PICK A THEME. IT COULD BE THINGS YOU'D SEE IN THE ZOO, ITEMS YOU'D TAKE ON HOLIDAY, THINGS YOU'D FIND IN THE SUPERMARKET, BOYS NAMES – ANYTHING YOU LIKE! CHOOSE SOMEONE TO START. THEY NEED TO NAME SOMETHING RELATED TO THE THEME YOU'VE CHOSEN BEGINNING WITH THE LETTER A. WORK YOUR WAY THROUGH THE ALPHABET, GOING AROUND THE PEOPLE IN THE CAR, TRYING TO FIND SOMETHING FOR EVERY LETTER. X AND Q ARE USUALLY THE HARDEST!

ABCDEFGHIJKLM
NOPQRSTUVWXYZ

YES OR NO?

THIS GAME IS HARDER THAN IT SOUNDS. ONE PERSON GETS CHOSEN AND THEY HAVE TO ANSWER QUESTIONS WITHOUT USING THE WORDS 'YES' OR 'NO'. EVERYONE ELSE CAN ASK ANYTHING THEY LIKE TO TRY AND GET THEM TO SLIP UP! THE WINNER IS THE ONE WHO LASTS THE LONGEST TIME WITHOUT SAYING 'YES' OR 'NO'.

YES! NO! YES! NO!

CAR COLOURS

EVERYONE IN THE CAR CHOOSES A DIFFERENT COLOUR. THE DRIVER STARTS THE RACE WITH THE WORDS: 'HOT WHEELS GO!' FROM THAT MOMENT ON AND FOR THE NEXT TEN MINUTES, EVERYONE HAS TO KEEP THEIR EYES ON THE ROAD TO SEE HOW MANY CARS THEY CAN SPOT IN THE COLOUR THEY'VE CHOSEN. THE WINNER IS THE ONE WHO SPOTS THE MOST CARS IN THEIR CHOSEN COLOUR!

CAR CHORTLES!

GET YOUR SENSE OF HUMOUR INTO GEAR WITH THESE HILARIOUS JOKES.

WHAT DO YOU CALL A COUNTRY WHERE EVERYONE DRIVES PINK CARS?
A PINK CAR-NATION!

WHEN IS A CAR NOT A CAR?
WHEN IT TURNS INTO A DRIVE!

WHAT SHOULD YOU DO IF YOU SEE A SPACEMAN?
PARK YOUR HOT WHEELS CAR IN IT, MAN!

WHAT KIND OF A SNAKE WOULD YOU FIND ON A CAR?
A WINDSCREEN VIPER!

WHAT DO YOU CALL A MAN WITH A CAR ON HIS HEAD?
JACK!

WHAT HAPPENS WHEN A FROG'S CAR BREAKS DOWN?
IT GETS TOAD AWAY!

WHAT DID THE JACK SAY TO THE CAR?
CAN I OFFER YOU A LIFT?

WHAT DID THE TRAFFIC LIGHTS SAY TO THE PEDESTRIAN?
DON'T STARE AT ME, I'M CHANGING!

MIXED UP MOTORS

THESE MOTORS HAVE GOT THEMSELVES INTO A BIT OF A MUDDLE! CAN YOU UNSCRAMBLE THE LETTERS ON THE NUMBER PLATES BELOW TO REVEAL THE NAMES OF SIX HOT WHEELS CARS? WRITE THE ANSWERS UNDERNEATH WHEN YOU KNOW THE ANSWER, THEN CHECK THE BACK OF THE BOOK TO SEE IF YOU'RE RIGHT.

TDVIRIE — rivired

ALBOWKOCHL — hollowback

RGEODR RGEODR — Rodgerdodger

KAJC RMEHAM — Jackhammer

ABLSINSE — Bassline

KERTCO XBO — Rocketbox

THE DRAG RACE

IT WAS A DARK AND STORMY DAY IN SAN DIEGO, USA. DOWN AT THE LOCAL DRAG RACE TRACK, THERE WAS TENSION IN THE AIR. TODAY'S RACE WAS GOING TO BE A HOT ONE. RATBOMB, RODGER DODGER, RIVITED AND PURPLE PASSION WERE RACING, AND THEY ALL WANTED TO BEAT THE COMPETITION TO BE THE CHAMPION!

THE CARS WERE IN THE PITS, HAVING THEIR FINAL CHECKS BEFORE THE RACE. THEIR MECHANICS WERE ALL WORKING HARD TO MAKE SURE THE ENGINES WERE TUNED TO PERFECTION. PURPLE PASSION'S MECHANIC QUICKLY HAD TO CHANGE A TYRE. IT WOULD BE A DISASTER IF PURPLE PASSION GOT A PUNCTURE!

THE DRAG RACE

THE STANDS WERE PACKED WITH FANS. THE CROWD
WAS HYPED UP WITH EXCITEMENT AND CHEERING
LOUDLY. PEOPLE WERE WAVING FLAGS AND
BANNERS, YELLING FOR THEIR FAVOURITE MOTORS.
"COME ON, RIVITED!"
"FLOOR IT, RODGER DODGER!"
"MAKE THEM EAT DUST, PURPLE PASSION!"
"BURN RUBBER, RATBOMB!"

THERE WERE JOURNALISTS FROM THE NEWSPAPERS EVERYWHERE, TRYING TO TALK TO THE DRIVERS OF THE CARS.
"WHO DO YOU THINK WILL WIN TODAY?" A REPORTER FROM THE SAN DIEGO STAR ASKED RATBOMB'S DRIVER.
"IT'S GOING TO BE A TIGHT RACE," RATBOMB'S DRIVER REPLIED. "THESE ARE GREAT CARS RACING TODAY AND THE COMPETITION IS FIERCE."
"I'LL BEAT THEM ALL," INTERRUPTED RIVITED'S DRIVER RUDELY. "I'M THE BEST AND I'VE GOT THE BEST CAR. OF COURSE I'LL WIN; NOBODY ELSE EVEN HAS A CHANCE!"

THE DRAG RACE

THE DRIVERS PUT ON THEIR RACING OVERALLS AND GRABBED THEIR HELMETS. THEY CLIMBED INTO THEIR CARS AND SWITCHED ON THE ENGINES. AS THE CARS PULLED UP TO THE STARTING LINE, THEIR WHEELS WERE SCREECHING AND LARGE CLOUDS OF SMOKE APPEARED FROM THEIR TYRES. THE CROWD WERE ON THE EDGE OF THEIR SEATS AND THE NOISE IN THE STADIUM WAS DEAFENING.

"I'M GOING TO LEAVE THE COMPETITION IN MY DUST," RIVITED'S DRIVER THOUGHT, CONFIDENTLY.

HE GLARED ACROSS AT THE DRIVER OF RODGER DODGER, WHO WAS LINED UP NEXT TO HIM.

A DEEP RUMBLE OF THUNDER ECHOED ABOVE
THE WAITING CARS. A FORK OF LIGHTING ZIPPED
THROUGH THE SKY.
VROOM! VROOM! THE THROATY ENGINES WERE
REVVING IMPATIENTLY AND THE NOISE WAS
VIBRATING THROUGH THE STADIUM.

THE DRAG RACE

THE RACE OFFICIAL WAS READY WITH HIS STARTER
BUTTON. HE LIFTED HIS FINGER, TOOK A DEEP
BREATH, THEN: BEEEEEEEEPPPPPP!
THE BUTTON WAS PRESSED. THE RACE WAS ON!
IN FRONT OF THE CARS, THE LIGHTS WERE
CHANGING. THE AMBER LIGHTS STARTED TO FLASH
AND THEN THE GREEN LIGHTS SHOWED. GO!
THEY WERE BURNIN' RUBBER!

BUT WAIT! A RED LIGHT WAS ON SHOW! WHAT A
DISASTER - THERE HAD BEEN A DISQUALIFICATION
BECAUSE ONE OF THE CARS HAD SET OFF BEFORE
THE GREEN LIGHTS.
THE CROWD HELD THEIR BREATH TO HEAR WHO
IT WAS...
"RIVITED HAS BEEN DISQUALIFIED," SAID THE RACE
OFFICIAL OVER THE LOUDSPEAKERS.
RIVITED'S DRIVER FURIOUSLY HIT THE BRAKES AND
THUMPED THE STEERING WHEEL IN ANGER.

THE DRAG RACE

THE REMAINING THREE CARS SPED ONWARDS DOWN
THE TRACK. AS THE RAIN STARTED TO POUR DOWN,
THE TRACK BECAME MORE AND MORE SLIPPERY.
PURPLE PASSION'S DRIVER SLAMMED HIS FOOT
DOWN ON THE ACCELERATOR, TRYING TO OVERTAKE
HIS RIVALS.
OH NO! TOO MUCH POWER!
PURPLE PASSION SKIDDED ACROSS THE TRACK AND
CRASHED INTO THE BARRIER. RACE OVER!

NOW THERE WERE JUST TWO CARS LEFT.
RATBOMB AND RODGER DODGER WHIZZED
ONWARDS AND THEY WERE VERY, VERY CLOSE.
THE DRIVERS' PEDALS WERE ON THE METAL AS
THEY STARED AHEAD, CONCENTRATING HARD.
FIRST RATBOMB WAS IN THE LEAD.
THEN IT WAS RODGER DODGER.
WHO WAS GOING TO WIN?

THE DRAG RACE

THE CARS SPED OVER THE FINISH LINE. IT WAS
TOO CLOSE TO CALL!
"WHO WON?" ASKED THE CROWD EXCITEDLY,
AS THEY EAGERLY WAITED FOR THE RESULTS.
"PHOTO FINISH," ANNOUNCED THE VOICE OVER
THE LOUDSPEAKERS.
EVERYONE GASPED. THE SUSPENSE
WAS INTENSE!

WINNER!

THE DRIVERS OF RATBOMB AND RODGER DODGER
SAT NERVOUSLY IN THEIR CARS. WHICH ONE OF
THEM WAS IT GOING TO BE?
THE LOUDSPEAKERS CRACKLED AGAIN. "I HAVE
THE RESULTS HERE. THE WINNER IS... RATBOMB!"
RATBOMB'S DRIVER WOUND DOWN THE WINDOW AND
PUNCHED HIS FIST TRIUMPHANTLY IN THE AIR.
YEAH! IT FELT GOOD TO BE THE BEST!

SCORCHING HOT DOT-TO-DOT

CIRCLE TRACKER HAS JUST SCREECHED TO A HALT – BUT WHY? JOIN UP THE DOTS 1-15, 17-28, 29-37, 39-48, 50-51, 53-56, 58-62, 64-67, 69-73, 75-93, 95-103, 105-123 & 125-128 TO FIND OUT!

RACING
ROCKET FIRE

ROCKET FIRE IS SPEEDING TOWARDS THE FINISH LINE OF A RACE. CAN YOU HELP THE CAR CHOOSE WHICH TRACK LEADS TO THE CHEQUERED FLAG?

GO!!!

1 2 3

JUMP INTO
THE DRIVER'S SEAT!

THESE HOT WHEELS ARE ZOOMING AROUND THE RACE TRACK AT TOP SPEED AND THEY ALL WANT TO BEAT THE COMPETITION! LOOK CAREFULLY AT THE PICTURES AND SEE IF YOU CAN SPOT THE EIGHT DIFFERENCES BETWEEN THEM. CHECK TO SEE IF YOU ARE RIGHT AT THE BACK OF THE BOOK.

MEGA MOTOR MEMORY GAME

LICENCE PLATE

SPEEDO

RACE FLAG

NUT

CAR KEYS

PARKING PERMIT

CAR STICKER

STEERING WHEEL

ALLOY WHEEL

SPANNER

DUST CAP

WRENCH

TEST YOUR MEMORY TO THE MAX WITH THIS FUN GAME. STARE AT THE IMAGES ON THIS PAGE, TRYING TO MEMORISE AS MANY AS YOU CAN, FOR 30 SECONDS. THEN COVER UP THE PICTURES WITH A SHEET OF PAPER AND WRITE DOWN AS MANY AS YOU CAN REMEMBER BELOW. HOW MANY DID YOU GET?

WHICH IS THE REAL FAST FISH?

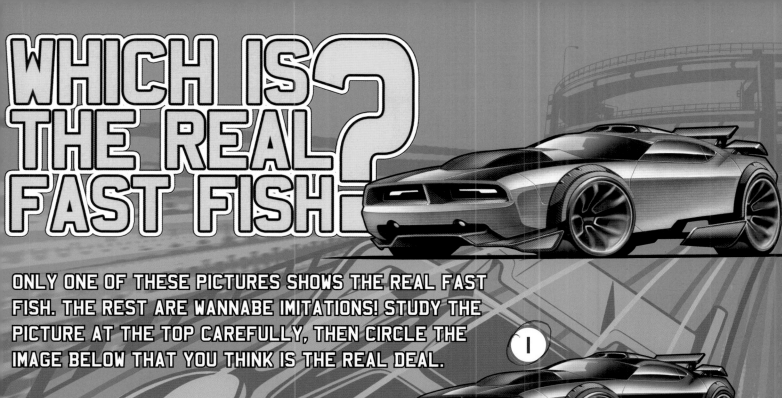

ONLY ONE OF THESE PICTURES SHOWS THE REAL FAST FISH. THE REST ARE WANNABE IMITATIONS! STUDY THE PICTURE AT THE TOP CAREFULLY, THEN CIRCLE THE IMAGE BELOW THAT YOU THINK IS THE REAL DEAL.

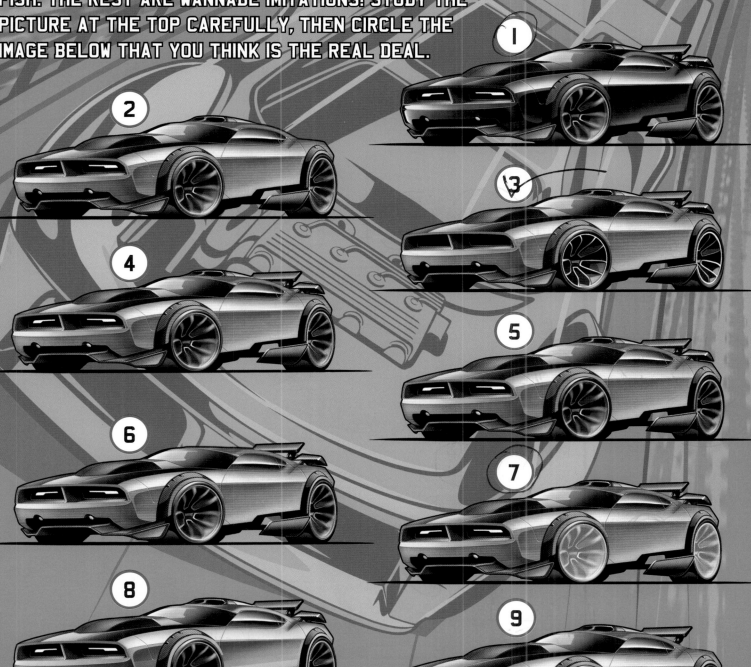

THIS HOT WHEELS MOTOR HAS COME INTO THE GARAGE FOR A TUNE-UP. NOT INCLUDING THE ONES ON THE CAR, CAN YOU COUNT HOW MANY TYRES ARE HIDDEN ON THIS PAGE? CHECK YOUR ANSWER AT THE BACK OF THE BOOK.

THERE ARE ???? HIDDEN TYRES.

TEST YOUR BRAIN SPEED

HERE'S A CHALLENGE TO TEST THE SPEED OF YOUR BRAIN.
HOW MANY NEW WORDS CAN YOU MAKE FROM THE LETTERS IN THE PHRASE BELOW?
THE RACE IS ON, SO SET YOURSELF A TIME-LIMIT OF THREE MINUTES! LET'S GO!

SPEEDING HOT WHEELS

EAT MY DUST!

OVERBOARD 454 IS A FORCE TO BE RECKONED WITH. IT CAN REACH CRAZILY FAST SPEEDS, SO BLINK AND YOU'LL MISS IT! USE YOUR PENS OR PENCILS TO COLOUR IN THIS AMAZING MOTOR THEN DRAW IN SOME SCENERY TO SHOW WHAT IT'S RACING PAST.

CRAZY CAR CROSSWORD

SOLVE THE CAR-RELATED CLUES TO FIND THE HOT WHEELS CAR HIDDEN IN THE SHADED SQUARES.

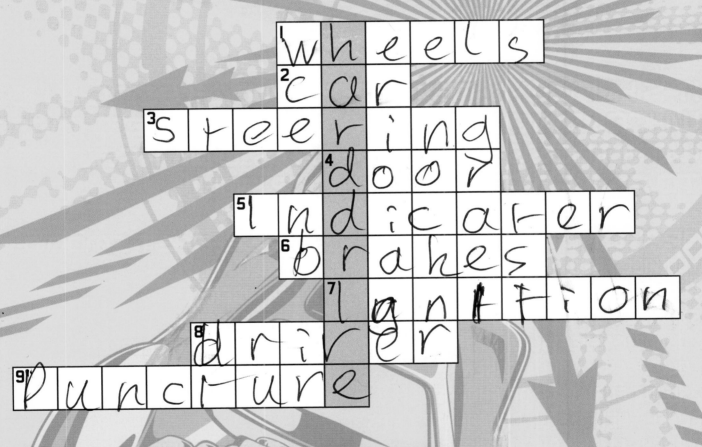

1. wheels
2. car
3. steering
4. door
5. indicater
6. brakes
7. ignition
8. driver
9. puncture

1. HOT _____ ARE THE COOLEST MOTORS AROUND!
2. ANOTHER WORD FOR MOTOR?
3. YOU USE THIS KIND OF WHEEL TO CONTROL WHAT DIRECTION YOU TRAVEL IN.
4. YOU OPEN THIS TO GET INTO A CAR.
5. YOU USE THESE TO SHOW WHICH WAY YOU WANT TO GO.
6. THESE ARE USED TO BRING YOUR CAR TO A STOP.
7. WHEN YOU START A CAR, YOU PUT YOUR KEYS IN THIS.
8. THE PERSON IN CHARGE OF THE CAR.
9. THIS CAN CAUSE A FLAT TYRE.

TIME FOR A PIT-STOP!

IT'S HUNGRY AND THIRSTY WORK BEING A HOT WHEELS DRIVER! GRAB SOME REFRESHMENT WITH THESE TASTY TREATS. DON'T FORGET TO ASK AN ADULT TO HELP YOU!

BRAKE FOR BISCUITS

YOU WILL NEED:
50G/2OZ PLAIN FLOUR
50G/2OZ BUTTER
25G/1OZ CASTER SUGAR
FEW DROPS VANILLA ESSENCE
25G/1OZ CURRANTS OR CHOPPED
GLACE CHERRIES OR CHOCOLATE CHIPS

1. PREHEAT THE OVEN TO 180C
2. CREAM TOGETHER BUTTER AND SUGAR.
3. SLOWLY MIX IN THE FLOUR.
4. ADD THE VANILLA ESSENCE.
5. MIX IN THE CURRANTS/GLACE
CHERRIES/CHOCOLATE CHIPS.
6. USING A SPOON, DROP SPOONFULS
OF THE MIXTURE ONTO A BAKING TRAY.
7. PLACE TRAY IN THE OVEN AND COOK
THE BISCUITS FOR 10 - 15 MINUTES
UNTIL LIGHTLY BROWNED.

SUPER-FAST SMOOTHIE

YOU WILL NEED:
4 STRAWBERRIES
10 RASPBERRIES
1 SMALL BANANA, CHOPPED
1 SMALL TUB OF A BERRY YOGHURT
1 CUP OF ORANGE JUICE

1. WASH THE BERRIES.
2. PUT THE BERRIES, ALONG WITH THE
JUICE AND YOGHURT, INTO A BLENDER.
3. BLEND UNTIL SMOOTH.
4. POUR INTO A GLASS AND ENJOY!

COOL CAR CHOCOLATE CRUNCHIES

YOU WILL NEED:
100G GOLDEN SYRUP
75G BUTTER
60G COOKING CHOCOLATE
50G RICE KRISPIES
50G ROLLED OATS
BUN TIN
BUN CASES

1. LINE A BUN TIN WITH BUN CASES.
2. PLACE THE SYRUP, BUTTER AND CHOCOLATE INTO A SMALL PAN AND MELT SLOWLY, OVER A LOW HEAT.
3. IN A SEPARATE BOWL, MIX TOGETHER THE RICE KRISPIES AND OATS, THEN ADD TO THE MIXTURE IN THE PAN.
4. REMOVE PAN FROM HEAT. USING A SPOON, PLACE A GENEROUS SPOONFUL OF MIXTURE IN EACH BUN CASE.
5. PLACE IN FRIDGE FOR AN HOUR TO ALLOW THE CRUNCHIES TO SET BEFORE SERVING.

PIT-STOP PIZZA

YOU WILL NEED:
1 NAAN BREAD PER PERSON
TOMATO PUREE/TOMATO KETCHUP
DRIED MIXED HERBS
SELECTION OF YOUR FAVOURITE TOPPINGS (SUCH AS PEPPERS, TOMATOES, MUSHROOMS, SWEETCORN, BROCCOLI, TUNA, PEPPERONI, COURGETTES, HAM, PINEAPPLE
CHEDDAR CHEESE

1. PREHEAT THE OVEN TO 200C/GAS MARK 6.
2. SPREAD A LAYER OF TOMATO PUREE/KETCHUP ONTO THE NAAN BREAD.
3. SPRINKLE ON SOME MIXED HERBS.
4. CHOP THE VEGETABLES INTO SMALL PIECES (IF USING) THEN ARRANGE THE TOPPINGS ONTO THE NAAN BREAD.
5. GRATE THE CHEDDAR CHEESE OVER THE TOP.
6. PLACE ON A BAKING TRAY AND COOK FOR 5-10 MINUTES UNTIL THE CHEESE IS MELTED AND GOLDEN BROWN.

DAYTONA RACEDAY

"GOOD AFTERNOON, LADIES AND GENTLEMEN, AND WELCOME TO THE WORLD FAMOUS DAYTONA RACE DAY. I KNOW YOU'RE ALL EXCITED ABOUT THE AMAZING EVENT WE'VE GOT LINED UP FOR YOU TODAY. SOME OF THE TOP CARS IN THE WORLD ARE RACING AND IT'S GOING TO BE A HOT ONE!"

"HERE COME THE CARS NOW AND THEIR ENGINES ARE REVVING HARD AS THEY WAIT AT THE STARTING GRID. YOU CAN FEEL THE TENSION IN THE AIR, BECAUSE EVERYONE WANTS TO BE A WINNER HERE TODAY. AMONGST THOSE ON THE TRACK WE CAN SEE LAST YEAR'S CHAMP, CIRCLE TRACKER, WHOSE DRIVER IS DETERMINED TO WIN THE TITLE FOR A SECOND YEAR."

"IN THE LINE-UP WE CAN ALSO SEE 24/SEVEN 1 AND 24/SEVEN 2 IN THE FRONT ROW. BOTH CARS HAVE BEEN PERFORMING STRONGLY IN RECENT RACES. JUST BEHIND IS OVERBOARD 454, A CAR THAT HAS A NEW TEAM OF MECHANICS AND IS DRIVING LIKE A DREAM. IT'LL BE INTERESTING TO SEE WHAT OVERBOARD 454 CAN DO OUT HERE TODAY."

"KEEP AN EYE ON THOSE LIGHTS, LADIES AND
GENTS, BECAUSE THEY'RE GOING TO BE CHANGING
COLOUR ANY SECOND NOW AND THE RACE IS GOING
TO START... AND THEY'RE OFF! CIRCLE TRACKER
HAS HAD A GREAT START AND IS POWERING AHEAD,
TAKING AN EARLY LEAD AND LEAVING THE REST
OF THE PACK BEHIND HIM."

"24/SEVEN I IS WEAVING BETWEEN THE CARS, GAINING PLACES AND MAKING UP LOST GROUND. THERE ARE NOW ONLY TWO CAR LENGTHS BETWEEN 24/SEVEN I AND CIRCLE TRACKER. AS CIRCLE TRACKER TRIES TO BLOCK 24/SEVEN I IT LOOKS LIKE THERE'S BEEN CONTACT BETWEEN THE TWO CARS. WHAT A DISASTER!"

"CIRCLE TRACKER HAS SPUN ACROSS THE TRACK AND IT SEEMS IT'S GAME OVER FOR THE MOTOR... BUT NO, I'M MISTAKEN. WOULD YOU LOOK AT THIS! THE DRIVER HAS SOMEHOW REGAINED CONTROL AND REJOINED THE RACE! THIS IS AMAZING STUFF! JUST WATCH AS CIRCLE TRACKER SPEEDS ONWARDS AS THOUGH NOTHING HAS HAPPENED. THAT'S THE SIGN OF A TRUE CHAMP."

"WHOA, THERE'S BEEN A HUGE PILE-UP! THIS IS CHAOS! I'D SAY MAYBE SIX OR SEVEN CARS HAVE BEEN TAKEN OUT, INCLUDING 24/SEVEN I! THIS HAS TURNED INTO A DESTRUCTION DERBY! 24/SEVEN I HAS BEEN A VICTIM OF THIS COLLISION AND HAS SWERVED INTO THE WALL. ITS RACE IS OVER, THE CAR'S TORN UP AND THE DRIVER WILL BE VERY, VERY DISAPPOINTED ABOUT THAT."

"WITH ONLY TWO LAPS LEFT TO GO, THIS IS SHAPING UP TO BE ONE OF THE BEST DAYTONA RACE DAYS IN HISTORY! JUST LOOK AT THEM ALL GO. ALL OF THE DRIVERS WANT THEIR CARS TO WIN, TO PROVE THAT THEY'RE THE CHAMPION AND BETTER THAN ALL THE REST. BUT WHICH ONE WILL SUCCEED? IT'S IMPOSSIBLE TO TELL AT THIS STAGE."

"WE HAVEN'T SEEN MUCH FROM OVERBOARD 454 YET HERE TODAY, THE CAR'S BEEN HANGING BACK A BIT, KEEPING OUT OF TROUBLE AND STAYING WITH THE PACK. BUT OVERBOARD 454 IS MOVING STEADILY THROUGH THE FIELD OF COMPETITORS NOW, PUTTING ON THE PRESSURE BY GOING LOW AND GAINING GROUND."

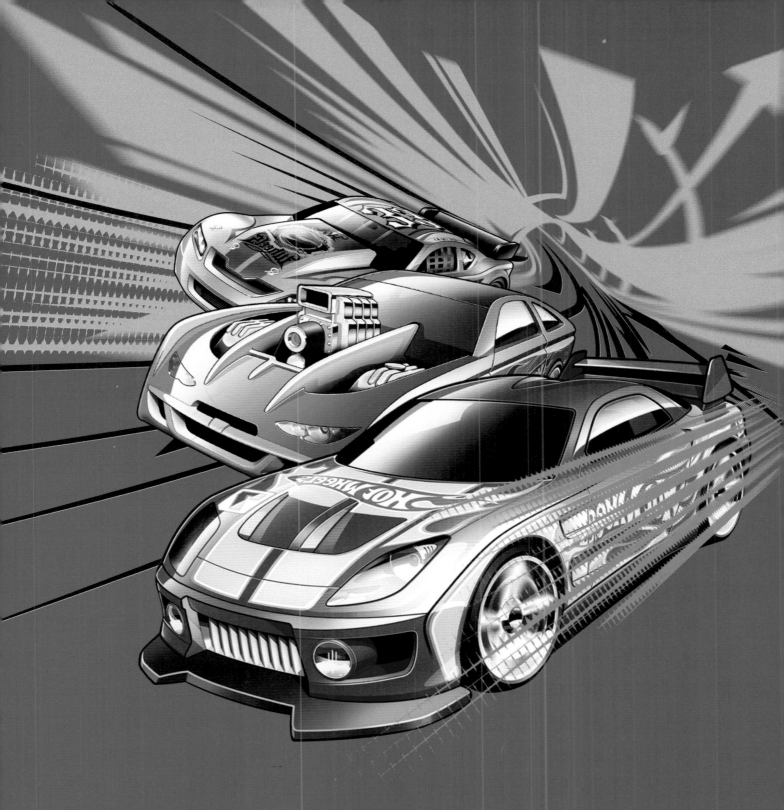

"WELL, LADIES AND GENTLEMEN, THIS IS IT, THE FINAL, NAIL-BITING LAP. THIS IS THE TIGHTEST RACE IN YEARS HERE ON DAYTONA RACE DAY! WE'VE GOT 24/SEVEN 2 CURRENTLY IN THE LEAD, CLOSELY FOLLOWED BY OVERBOARD 454 AND CIRCLE TRACKER IN THIRD."

"THESE THREE CARS ARE ALL BATTLING FOR THE
LEAD AND IT'S VERY CLOSE INDEED. I THINK
24/SEVEN 2 MIGHT JUST TAKE IT... BUT NO! WAIT
A MINUTE! OVERBOARD 454 IS PULLING OUT AND
MOVING TO OVERTAKE. THIS IS A VERY BRAVE
MOVE AT SUCH A LATE STAGE IN THE RACE.
BUT IT'S PAID OFF, 24/SEVEN 2 HAS BEEN BUMPED
DOWN INTO SECOND PLACE!"

"I CAN'T BELIEVE MY EYES! AT THE VERY LAST MINUTE, OVERBOARD 454 HAS TAKEN THE LEAD AND CLINCHED THE CHAMPIONSHIP. THE DAYTONA RACE CUP BELONGS TO OVERBOARD 454! ONCE AGAIN, I REPEAT, OVERBOARD 454 IS THE WINNER. 24/SEVEN 2 CAME IN SECOND WHILE CIRCLE TRACKER WAS THIRD. CONGRATULATIONS, OVERBOARD 454, AND WHAT AN OUTSTANDING RACE!"

PETROL STOP

OH NO! PURPLE PASSION IS ALMOST OUT OF PETROL. HELP THIS HOT WHEELS FAVOURITE CHOOSE THE CORRECT ROAD TO GET TO THE PETROL STATION BEFORE ITS TANK RUNS DRY.

PETROL

HOT WHEELS

HUNT THE... HOT WHEELS

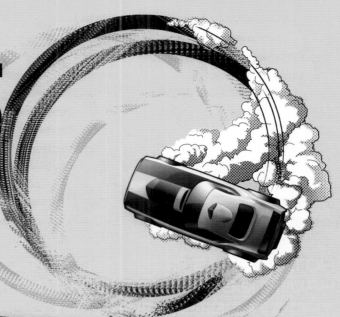

LOOK AT THIS WORDSEARCH SQUARE AND SEE IF YOU CAN FIND ALL THESE HOT WHEELS CARS. THE WORDS READ ACROSS, DOWN, BACKWARDS AND FORWARDS.

H	A	Y	E	N	I	L	S	S	A	B	N
A	H	O	L	L	O	W	B	A	C	K	O
R	W	A	V	N	B	F	G	J	W	X	U
D	E	W	I	S	W	A	D	F	S	O	M
D	R	E	K	A	H	S	E	N	O	B	Q
R	W	R	B	C	G	T	W	A	N	T	R
I	K	R	E	W	Q	F	I	T	K	E	S
V	D	E	T	I	V	I	R	F	D	K	Y
E	W	D	R	A	G	S	T	E	R	C	I
X	E	P	U	R	L	H	K	J	T	O	P
S	P	I	N	E	B	U	S	T	E	R	Z
V	B	N	W	T	W	I	N	M	I	L	L

BASSLINE		☑ HOLLOWBACK	☐
BONE SHAKER		☑ RIVITED	☐
DRAGSTER		☑ ROCKET BOX	☐
FAST FISH		☑ SPINE BUSTER	☐
HARD DRIVE		☑ TWIN MILL	☐

SPOT THE FAKE!

HOT WHEELS CARS ARE IMPRESSIVE RIDES. SOME SNEAKY CRIMINALS HAVE TRIED TO COPY THE MOTORS AND IT'S TIME TO GET THEM OFF THE STREETS! ONLY THREE CARS IN EACH ROW ARE GENUINE, THE OTHER IS A FAKE. LOOK CAREFULLY AT THE PICTURES BELOW AND DRAW A CIRCLE ROUND THE ODD ONE OUT IN EACH ROW.

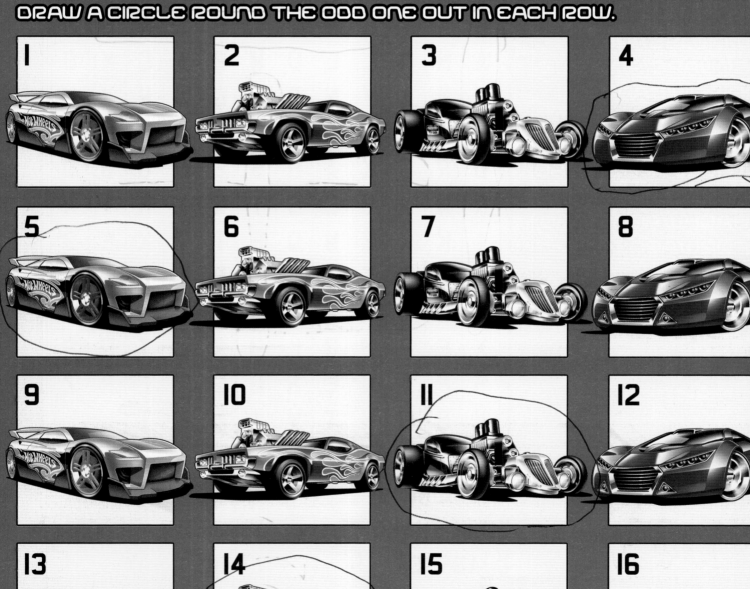

HOT WHEELS™
WORD MATCH

SEE IF YOU CAN MATCH THE WORDS ON THE LEFT TO THE ONES ON THE RIGHT TO MAKE THE NAMES OF EIGHT WELL-KNOWN HOT WHEELS CARS. THE ANSWERS ARE AT THE BACK OF YOUR BOOK.

FAST	HAMMER
CIRCLE	SHAKER
RODGER	ONE
COOL	RACE
SOOO	DODGER
BONE	FAST
JACK	FISH
ULTRA	TRACKER

COLOUR THE CARS!

HOT WHEELS CARS ARE THE FASTEST, SNAZZIEST AND COOLEST MOTORS AROUND! USE YOUR PENS OR PENCILS TO COLOUR THEM IN BY NUMBERS, USING THE KEY SHOWN.

24 SEVEN

1	2
3	4
5	6

NITRO SCORCHER

1	2
3	4
5	6

MATCH 24/SEVEN

YOU'D BETTER BUCKLE UP BECAUSE 24/SEVEN IS AN AWESOME RIDE! LOOK AT THESE PICTURES AND USE A PENCIL TO JOIN UP THE PAIRS THAT MATCH. DRAW A CIRCLE AROUND THE ONE THAT IS LEFT OVER.

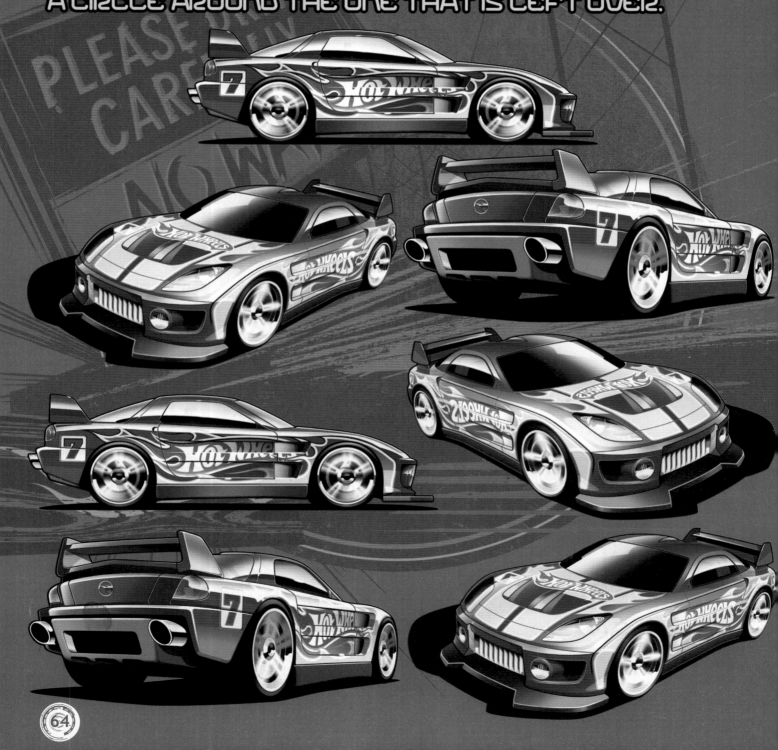

NUMBER 1

HOT WHEELS™

FAN!

DO YOU THINK YOU'RE THE BIGGEST FAN OF HOT WHEELS? WRITE ALL ABOUT IT BELOW... HERE!

MY NAME IS _____

I AM _____ YEARS-OLD.

I OWN _____ HOT WHEELS CARS.

MY FAVOURITE HOT WHEELS

CAR IS _____

I LIKE IT BEST BECAUSE _____

_____

WHAT COLOUR IS IT? _____

DOES YOUR FAVOURITE HOT

WHEELS CAR HAVE SNAZZY

BODYWORK? IF SO, WHAT KIND

OF PATTERN DOES IT HAVE?

_____

USE TWO WORDS TO DESCRIBE

IT: _____ AND _____

I AM THE NUMBER ONE HOT

WHEELS FAN BECAUSE _____

_____

SOOO FAST VS ZOTIC MAZE

CAN YOU HEAR THE ENGINES REVVING? SOOO FAST AND ZOTIC ARE READY TO RACE! GRAB A FRIEND, CHOOSE WHO'S GOING TO BE SOOO FAST AND WHO'S GOING TO BE ZOTIC, THEN SEE WHO GETS TO THE FINISH LINE FIRST BY STEERING THROUGH THE PATHS OF THE MAZE.

THE RING OF FIRE

THE CROWD HAD GATHERED IN THE STADIUM AT THE ANNUAL HOT WHEELS TRICKS EVENT. THEY WERE WHOOPING AND HOLLERING. EVERYONE KNEW THEY WERE IN FOR A TREAT. THEY'D SEE HOLLOWBACKS PERFORMING ALL KINDS OF AMAZING TRICKS AND STUNTS. THE AMAZING HOLLOWBACKS WOULD JUMP CARS, DO THE LOOP-THE-LOOP AND IN THE FINALE, WOULD TRY TO LEAP THROUGH THE TERRIFYING RING OF FIRE.

TWO HOLLOWBACKS DROVE
OUT INTO THE ARENA.
THE DRIVERS NODDED
AT ONE ANOTHER, THEN
SLAMMED DOWN ON THEIR
ACCELERATORS. THE CARS
CRISS-CROSSED AROUND
EACH OTHER, THEN MOVED
IN SYNCHRONISATION TO
SLIDE IN TWO PERFECTLY
EXECUTED CIRCLES. THE
DRIVERS JUMPED OUT OF
THE CARS AND HIGH-FIVED.

THE HOLLOWBACK'S DRIVER CLIMBED BACK IN THE CAR AND FLOORED THE ACCELERATOR. THE CAR'S TYRES SCREAMED AS THE CAR LEAPT FORWARDS. THE HOLLOWBACK ZOOMED ALONG THE LENGTH OF THE STADIUM, THEN UP A RAMP AND ONTO TWO WHEELS! THE CAR RACED ALONG BEFORE RETURNING SAFELY TO THE GROUND. THE CROWD GASPED IN AMAZEMENT. THESE TRICKS WERE SCORCHIN'!

NEXT, SIX CARS LINED UP
NEXT TO A LARGE RAMP.
THE HOLLOWBACK'S ENGINE
REVVED. IT WAS TIME FOR
SOME JUMPING!
THE HOLLOWBACK SPED
UP THE RAMP AND FLEW
THROUGH THE AIR. IT
LANDED SAFELY ON THE
OTHER SIDE OF THE CARS
WITH ROOM TO SPARE.
YOWSER! EVERYONE
AGREED THE HOT WHEELS
CARS SURE COULD MOVE!

THE SPECTATORS CLAPPED AND CHEERED THEIR APPROVAL. THEN SOME MORE VEHICLES JOINED THE LINE-UP. NOW THERE WERE TEN CARS! SURELY THE HOLLOWBACK COULDN'T JUMP THEM ALL? OH YES IT COULD! THE HOLLOWBACK WENT LIKE A BULLET UP THE RAMP AND OVER THE TEN CARS WITH EASE.

NEXT, A HOLLOWBACK APPROACHED THE LOOP-THE-LOOP WHERE THE CAR PAUSED. THE HOLLOWBACK'S DRIVER REVVED THE ENGINE FIERCELY.

VROOOM! VROOOM! THE CROWD GASPED. SURELY THE HOLLOWBACK WASN'T GOING TO ATTEMPT THE 360 DEGREE LOOP? YES! IT WAS!

THE HOLLOWBACK'S DRIVER FROWNED IN CONCENTRATION. THIS WAS A TOUGH TRICK, ONE OF THE MOST DIFFICULT AROUND. THERE WAS NO MARGIN FOR MISTAKES. THE HOLLOWBACK WAS GOING TO DO ONE OF THE MOST DANGEROUS STUNTS AROUND.

THE DRIVER JAMMED HIS FOOT ONTO THE ACCELERATOR AND THE CAR SPED OFF, FASTER AND FASTER. IT WAS CRUCIAL THAT IT GAINED ENOUGH SPEED AND MOMENTUM TO MAKE IT ROUND THE LOOP-THE-LOOP.

NEEEEE-YOOOOOOOWWWWW!
THE HOLLOWBACK ZIPPED
ALONG THE TRACK AND
WAS AROUND THE LOOP-
THE-LOOP IN THE BLINK
OF AN EYE. THE CROWD
WENT WILD, YELLING AND
STAMPING THEIR FEET.
THEY COULD HARDLY
BELIEVE WHAT THEY'D
JUST SEEN.
WHAT AN AMAZING TRICK!
THE HOLLOWBACK'S STUNT
ACTION HAD PROPELLED
THE CAR TO NEW HEIGHTS!
THE DRIVER CLENCHED HIS
FIST WITH DELIGHT.

IT WAS FINALLY TIME FOR THE LAST TRICK OF THE DAY. IT WAS THE HARDEST STUNT A CAR COULD DO, AND THE MOST DANGEROUS THING A DRIVER COULD ASK OF THEIR VEHICLE. IT WAS TIME TO ATTEMPT THE RING OF FIRE! THE CROWD FELL SILENT WITH ANTICIPATION.

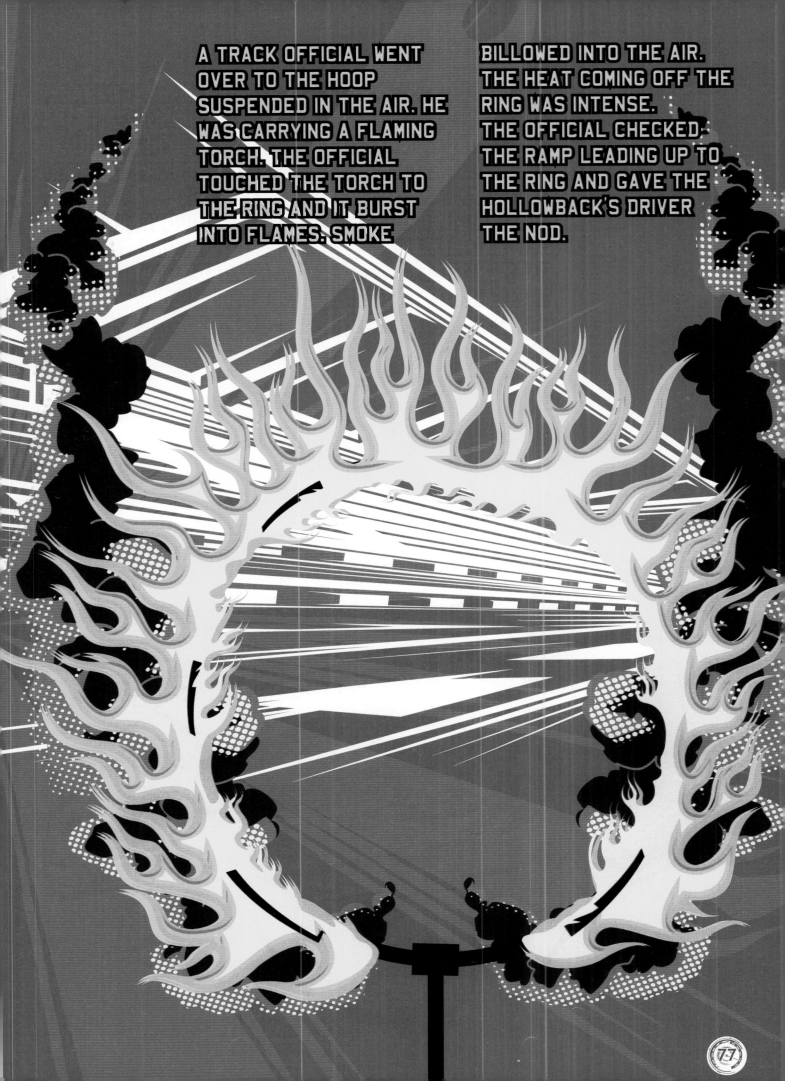

A TRACK OFFICIAL WENT OVER TO THE HOOP SUSPENDED IN THE AIR. HE WAS CARRYING A FLAMING TORCH. THE OFFICIAL TOUCHED THE TORCH TO THE RING AND IT BURST INTO FLAMES. SMOKE BILLOWED INTO THE AIR. THE HEAT COMING OFF THE RING WAS INTENSE. THE OFFICIAL CHECKED THE RAMP LEADING UP TO THE RING AND GAVE THE HOLLOWBACK'S DRIVER THE NOD.

THE RING OF FIRE

THE HOLLOWBACK'S ENGINE REVVED. THE CROWD STARTED SLOW CLAPPING AS THEY URGED THE CAR ON. THE HOLLOWBACK SET OFF AND BEGAN TO GATHER SPEED. THE CAR GOT FASTER... FASTER... AND FASTER...

THEN THE HOLLOWBACK WAS ZOOMING UP THE RAMP, THROUGH THE RING OF FIRE AND FLYING THROUGH THE AIR! THE HOLLOWBACK LANDED WITH A BOUNCE AND ROARED AROUND THE STADIUM DOING A LAP OF VICTORY.

YEAH! WHAT A SUCCESS!
THE CROWD WENT
WILD, APPLAUDING AND
CHEERING THE AMAZING
HOLLOWBACKS.
WHAT AWESOME MOTORS!

ONLY THE BEST HOT
WHEELS CARS COULD DO
INCREDIBLE STUNTS LIKE
THAT! HOT WHEELS ARE
THE BEST!

SCORCHIN' 2010
HOT WHEELS CALENDAR

WHAT A SMOKIN' HOT CALENDAR! USE THE SPACES TO WRITE DOWN ALL YOUR IMPORTANT DATES AND STUFF YOU NEED TO REMEMBER.

JANUARY

MONDAY	TUESDAY	WEDNESDAY	THURSDAY	FRIDAY	SATURDAY	SUNDAY
				1	2	3
4	5	6	7	8	9	10
11	12	13	14	15	16	17
18	19	20	21	22	23	24
25	26	27	28	29	30	31

APRIL

MONDAY	TUESDAY	WEDNESDAY	THURSDAY	FRIDAY	SATURDAY	SUNDAY
			1	2	3	4
5	6	7	8	9	10	11
12	13	14	15	16	17	18
19	20	21	22	23	24	25
26	27	28	29	30		

FEBRUARY

MONDAY	TUESDAY	WEDNESDAY	THURSDAY	FRIDAY	SATURDAY	SUNDAY
1	2	3	4	5	6	7
8	9	10	11	12	13	14
15	16	17	18	19	20	21
22	23	24	25	26	27	28

MAY

MONDAY	TUESDAY	WEDNESDAY	THURSDAY	FRIDAY	SATURDAY	SUNDAY
					1	2
3	4	5	6	7	8	9
10	11	12	13	14	15	16
17	18	19	20	21	22	23
24	25	26	27	28	29	30
31						

MARCH

MONDAY	TUESDAY	WEDNESDAY	THURSDAY	FRIDAY	SATURDAY	SUNDAY
1	2	3	4	5	6	7
8	9	10	11	12	13	14
15	16	17	18	19	20	21
22	23	24	25	26	27	28
29	30	31				

JUNE

MONDAY	TUESDAY	WEDNESDAY	THURSDAY	FRIDAY	SATURDAY	SUNDAY
	1	2	3	4	5	6
7	8	9	10	11	12	13
14	15	16	17	18	19	20
21	22	23	24	25	26	27
28	29	30				

JULY

MONDAY	TUESDAY	WEDNESDAY	THURSDAY	FRIDAY	SATURDAY	SUNDAY
			1	2	3	4
5	6	7	8	9	10	11
12	13	14	15	16	17	18
19	20	21	22	23	24	25
26	27	28	29	30	31	

OCTOBER

MONDAY	TUESDAY	WEDNESDAY	THURSDAY	FRIDAY	SATURDAY	SUNDAY
				1	2	3
4	5	6	7	8	9	10
11	12	13	14	15	16	17
18	19	20	21	22	23	24
25	26	27	28	29	30	31

AUGUST

MONDAY	TUESDAY	WEDNESDAY	THURSDAY	FRIDAY	SATURDAY	SUNDAY
						1
2	3	4	5	6	7	8
9	10	11	12	13	14	15
16	17	18	19	20	21	22
23	24	25	26	27	28	29
30	31					

NOVEMBER

MONDAY	TUESDAY	WEDNESDAY	THURSDAY	FRIDAY	SATURDAY	SUNDAY
1	2	3	4	5	6	7
8	9	10	11	12	13	14
15	16	17	18	19	20	21
22	23	24	25	26	27	28
29	30					

SEPTEMBER

MONDAY	TUESDAY	WEDNESDAY	THURSDAY	FRIDAY	SATURDAY	SUNDAY
		1	2	3	4	5
6	7	8	9	10	11	12
13	14	15	16	17	18	19
20	21	22	23	24	25	26
27	28	29	30			

DECEMBER

MONDAY	TUESDAY	WEDNESDAY	THURSDAY	FRIDAY	SATURDAY	SUNDAY
		1	2	3	4	5
6	7	8	9	10	11	12
13	14	15	16	17	18	19
20	21	22	23	24	25	26
27	28	29	30	31		

COPY THE CARS

COPYING PICTURES IS MUCH EASIER WITH A GRID TO HELP YOU! CHECK OUT THESE PICTURES OF TWIN MILL AND RATBOMB. GRAB A PENCIL AND USE THE GRIDS TO HELP YOU COPY THE IMAGES SQUARE-BY-SQUARE.

BE A...
RACE OFFICIAL

THE OFFICIALS IN CHARGE OF THE HOT WHEELS RACES HAVE THE BEST JOB IN THE WORLD. THEY GET TO WATCH ALL OF THE HOT WHEELS COMPETITIONS AND AWARD THE WINNING CARS WITH THEIR MEDALS. NOW IT'S YOUR TURN TO BE A HOT WHEELS RACE OFFICIAL. GRAB YOUR FAVOURITE HOT WHEELS MOTORS, STAGE A RACE, THEN WRITE ALL ABOUT IT HERE!

HOT WHEELS SPEEDSTER RACE!

NAME OF RACE OFFICIAL:

THE WINNING CAR WAS:

THE CAR IN SECOND PLACE WAS:

THE CAR IN THIRD PLACE WAS:

THE WINNING TIME WAS:

THE FASTEST SPEED REACHED WAS:

WAS ANYONE DISQUALIFIED?

IF SO, WHY?

THE WINNER'S PODIUM!

WELCOME TO THE WINNER'S ENCLOSURE. THE MEDAL PRESENTATIONS ARE JUST ABOUT TO START. DRAW THE CARS THAT CAME FIRST, SECOND AND THIRD IN THE APPROPRIATE PLACES ON THE PODIUM, THEN DESIGN THE MEDALS THEY'LL BE AWARDED.

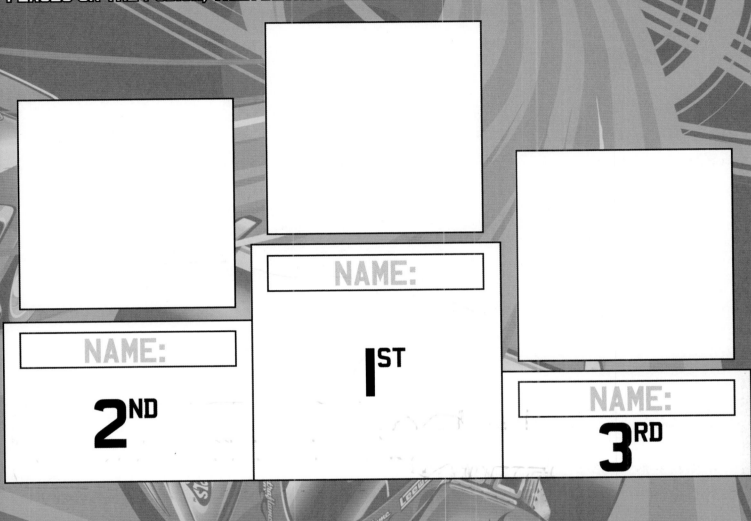

NAME:

1ST

NAME:

2ND

NAME:

3RD

THE RACE IS ON!

YOU HAVE TO STOP AT A RED LIGHT! GO BACK THREE SPACES.

FINISH

THE ROAD AHEAD IS CLEAR. SPEED FORWARD FOUR SPACES.

THERE'S OIL ON THE ROAD AND YOU SKID! GO BACK TWO SPACES.

YOU ACCELERATE - ZOOM FORWARD TWO SPACES.

CHOOSE A COUNTER OF A DIFFERENT COLOUR FOR EACH PLAYER. PLACE THE COUNTERS ON THE START. EACH THROW THE DICE. THE PERSON WHO ROLLS THE HIGHEST NUMBER GOES FIRST. TAKE IT IN TURNS TO THROW THE DICE AND WORK YOUR WAY ALONG THE RACE TRACK TOWARDS THE CHEQUERED FLAG. THE FIRST ONE TO CROSS THE FINISH LINE IS THE WINNER.

MPH km/h

HOT WHEELS

YOU HAVE TO STOP AT A RED LIGHT! GO BACK THREE SPACES.

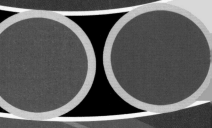

THE HOT WHEELS RACE IS ABOUT TO START! THE CARS ARE REVVING THEIR ENGINES AND THEY'RE READY TO GO. FIND A DICE AND COUNTERS SO THAT YOU AND YOUR FRIENDS CAN JOIN THE RACE.

START

YOU ACCELERATE - ZOOM FORWARD TWO SPACES.

THERE'S OIL ON THE ROAD AND YOU SKID! GO BACK TWO SPACES.

YOU HAVE TO PULL OVER FOR A PIT-STOP. MISS ONE TURN.

YOUR ENGINE HAS BEEN FINELY TUNED TO PERFECTION. GO FORWARD FIVE SPACES.

THE ROAD AHEAD IS CLEAR. SPEED FORWARD FOUR SPACES.

HOT WHEELS IN THE CITY

THE HOT WHEELS CARS ARE CRUISING THROUGH THE CITY STREETS! LOOK AT THE PICTURE AND SEE IF YOU CAN SPOT ALL THESE DETAILS IN IT. TICK EACH ONE OFF AS YOU FIND IT.

URBAN MISSION

IN JAPAN, DARK HAS FALLEN AND THE STREETS HAVE BEEN CLEARED. IT'S TIME FOR ONE OF THE MOST EXCITING NIGHT STREET RACES AROUND - THE URBAN MISSION! THERE ARE GOING TO BE THREE HOT RACES. THESE CARS ARE GOING TO BURN SOME SERIOUS RUBBER HERE TONIGHT.

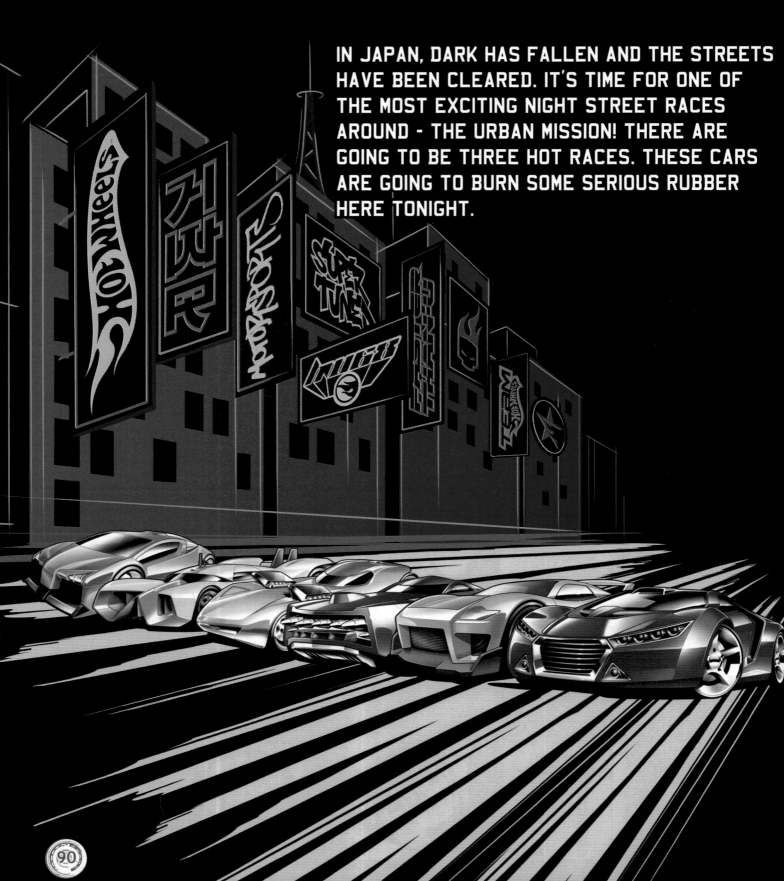

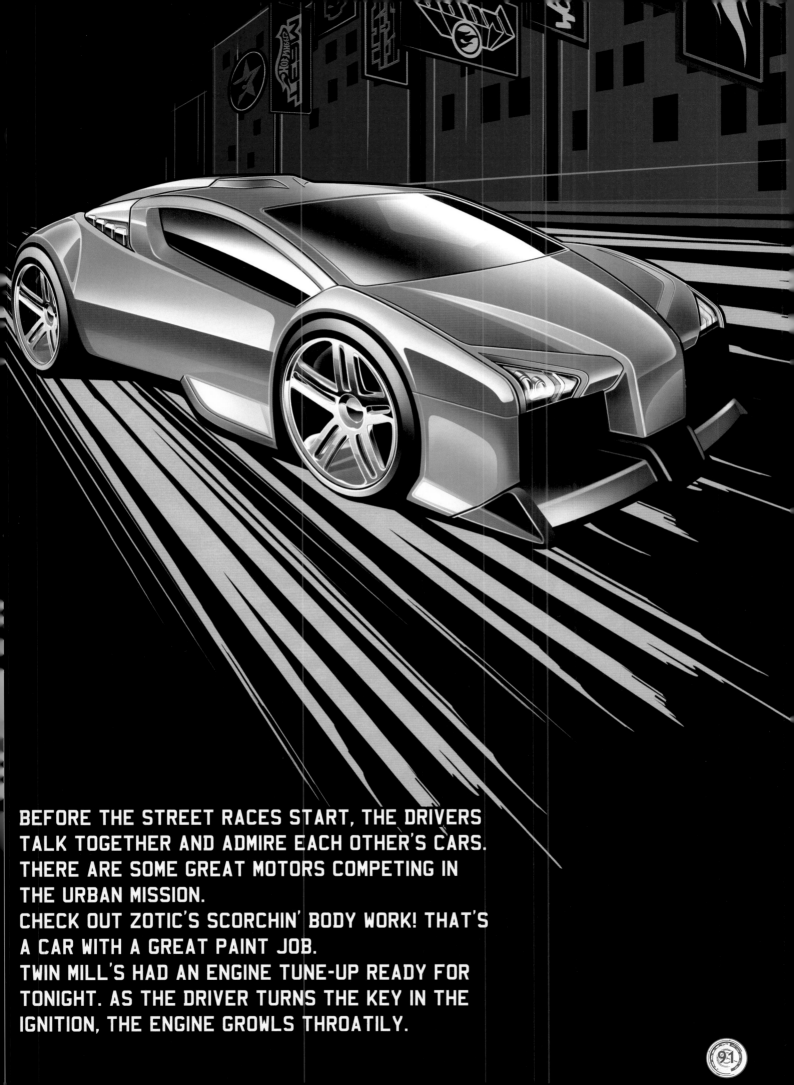

BEFORE THE STREET RACES START, THE DRIVERS
TALK TOGETHER AND ADMIRE EACH OTHER'S CARS.
THERE ARE SOME GREAT MOTORS COMPETING IN
THE URBAN MISSION.
CHECK OUT ZOTIC'S SCORCHIN' BODY WORK! THAT'S
A CAR WITH A GREAT PAINT JOB.
TWIN MILL'S HAD AN ENGINE TUNE-UP READY FOR
TONIGHT. AS THE DRIVER TURNS THE KEY IN THE
IGNITION, THE ENGINE GROWLS THROATILY.

URBAN MISSION

RACE ONE: URBAN AGENT VS ZOTIC!
URBAN AGENT AND ZOTIC ARE GOING TO BE THE
FIRST CARS TO RACE. THE DRIVERS OF THE
VEHICLES STARE STRAIGHT AHEAD. THEY'RE
FOCUSED ON ONLY ONE THING – WINNING THE RACE.
THEIR ENGINES ARE ROARING FIERCELY AND THE
CARS ARE PREPARED FOR THE OFF.
RACE NUMBER ONE – CARS GET READY!

TWIN MILL'S HORN SOUNDS THREE TIMES.
BEEP! BEEP! BEEEEEEEEP!
THE THIRD TIME THE HORN BLARES, URBAN AGENT
AND ZOTIC SPEED AWAY. URBAN AGENT'S TYRES
SPIN AND THE CAR LOSES VALUABLE SECONDS.
ZOTIC GAINS GROUND AND ZOOMS AHEAD.
URBAN AGENT'S DRIVER SLAMS DOWN THE
ACCELERATOR AND CHANGES GEAR.
URBAN AGENT IS GAINING ON ZOTIC!

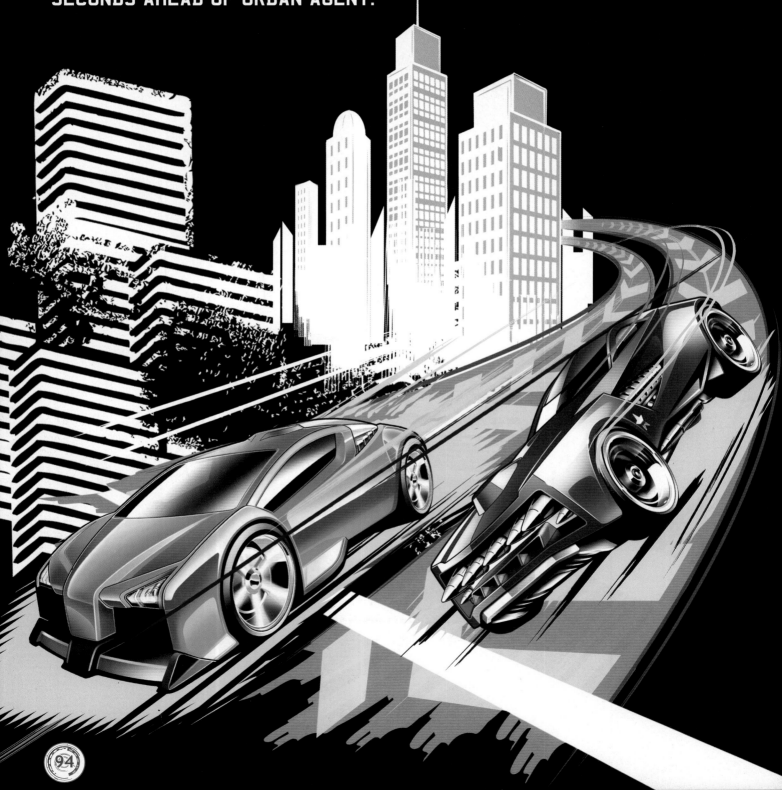

URBAN
MISSION

AS THE CARS SCREAM THROUGH THE STREETS, URBAN AGENT IS HOT ON ZOTIC'S TAIL. URBAN AGENT IS CATCHING UP BUT IT'S NOT ENOUGH. ZOTIC'S OBTAINED TOO MUCH OF A LEAD AND CRUISES OVER THE FINISH LINE SEVERAL SECONDS AHEAD OF URBAN AGENT.

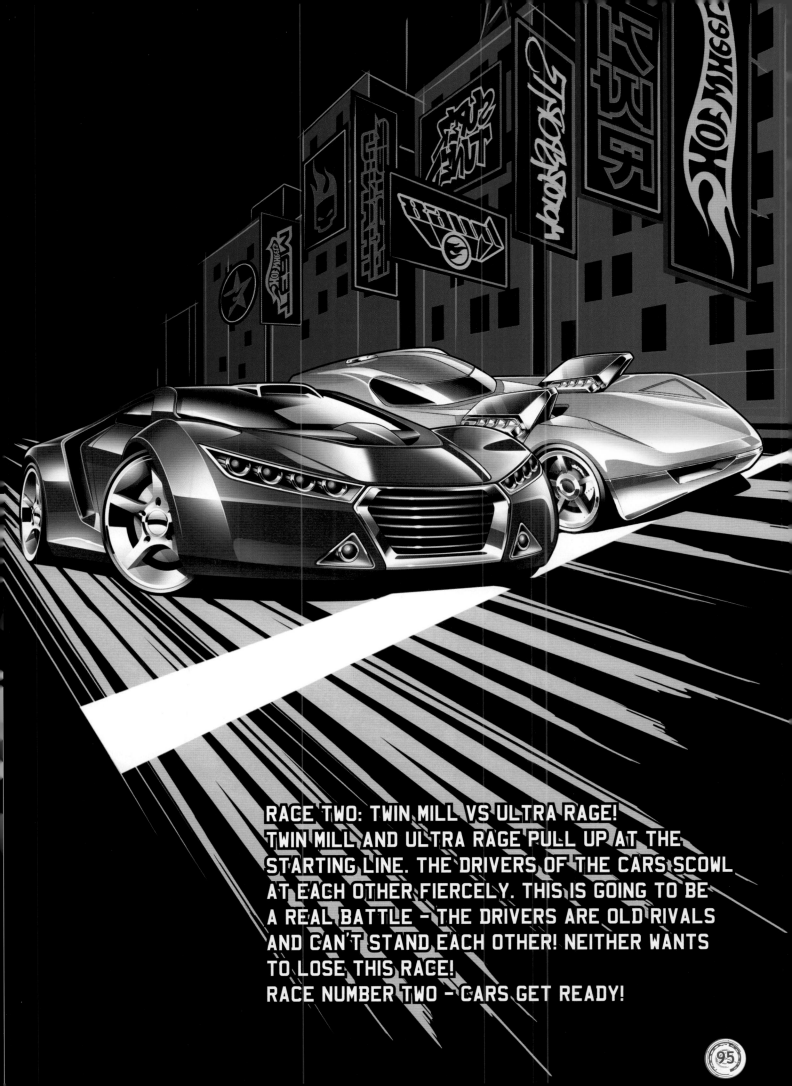

RACE TWO: TWIN MILL VS ULTRA RAGE!
TWIN MILL AND ULTRA RAGE PULL UP AT THE
STARTING LINE. THE DRIVERS OF THE CARS SCOWL
AT EACH OTHER FIERCELY. THIS IS GOING TO BE
A REAL BATTLE – THE DRIVERS ARE OLD RIVALS
AND CAN'T STAND EACH OTHER! NEITHER WANTS
TO LOSE THIS RACE!
RACE NUMBER TWO – CARS GET READY!

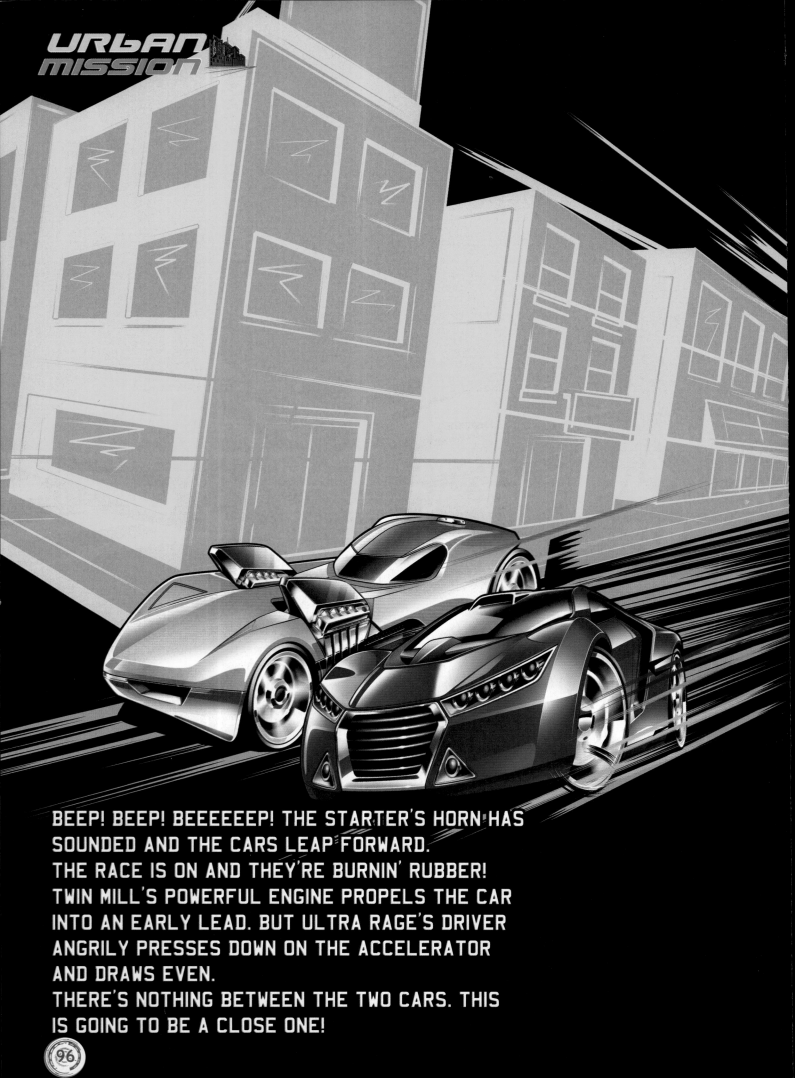

BEEP! BEEP! BEEEEEEP! THE STARTER'S HORN HAS
SOUNDED AND THE CARS LEAP FORWARD.
THE RACE IS ON AND THEY'RE BURNIN' RUBBER!
TWIN MILL'S POWERFUL ENGINE PROPELS THE CAR
INTO AN EARLY LEAD. BUT ULTRA RAGE'S DRIVER
ANGRILY PRESSES DOWN ON THE ACCELERATOR
AND DRAWS EVEN.
THERE'S NOTHING BETWEEN THE TWO CARS. THIS
IS GOING TO BE A CLOSE ONE!

DISASTER! TWIN MILL HAS GOT A PUNCTURE!
TWIN MILL STARTS TO SWERVE AND THE DRIVER
STRUGGLES TO GAIN CONTROL OF THE CAR. TWIN
MILL'S DRIVER FIGHTS WITH THE STEERING WHEEL
BUT HIS CAR'S FALLING TOO FAR BEHIND.

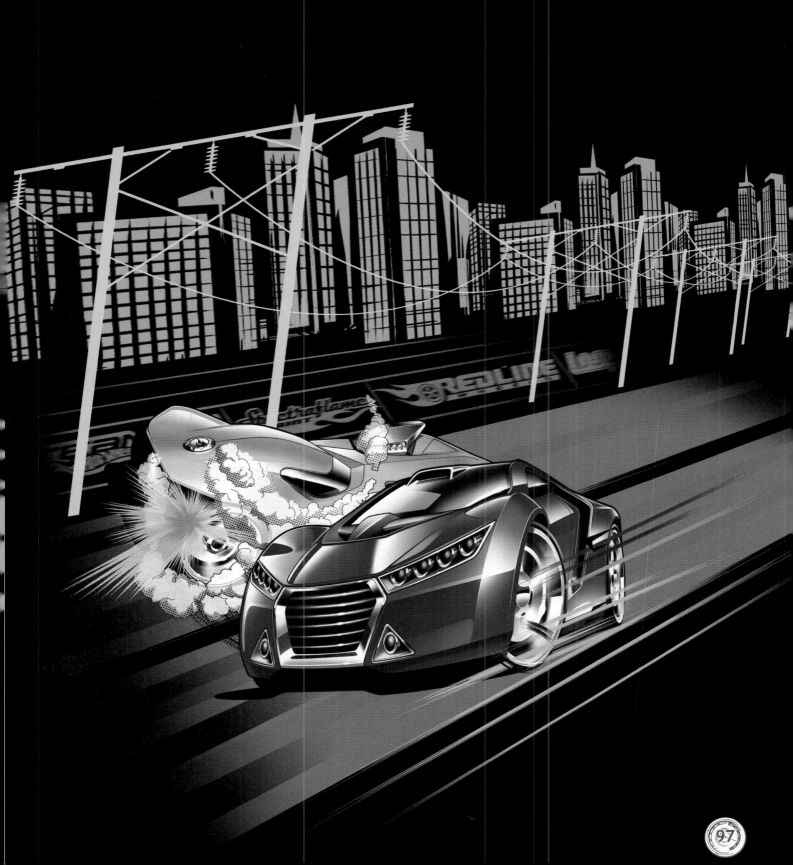

TWIN MILL BOUNCES INTO THE KERB AND IT'S OFFICIAL. TWIN MILL'S RACE IS OVER AND THE CAR'S LEFT EATING ULTRA RAGE'S DUST! TWIN MILL'S DRIVER GROANS WITH DISAPPOINTMENT AND DROPS HIS HEAD INTO HIS HANDS. IN THE DISTANCE, ULTRA RAGE RACES ACROSS THE FINISH LINE AND GRABS THE VICTORY.
RACE NUMBER TWO: ULTRA RAGE IS THE WINNER!

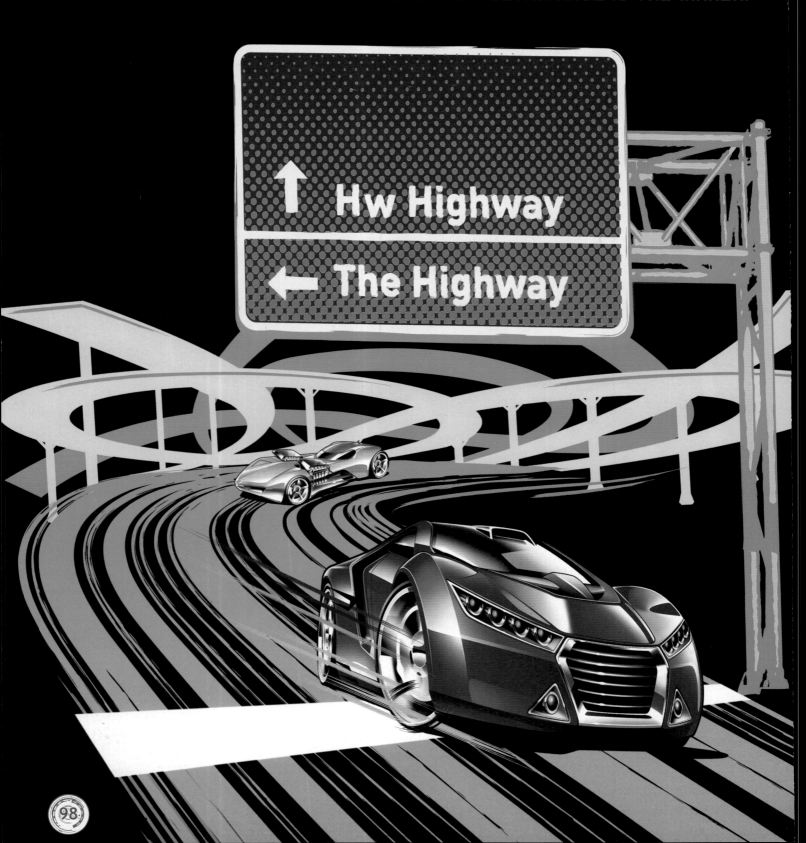

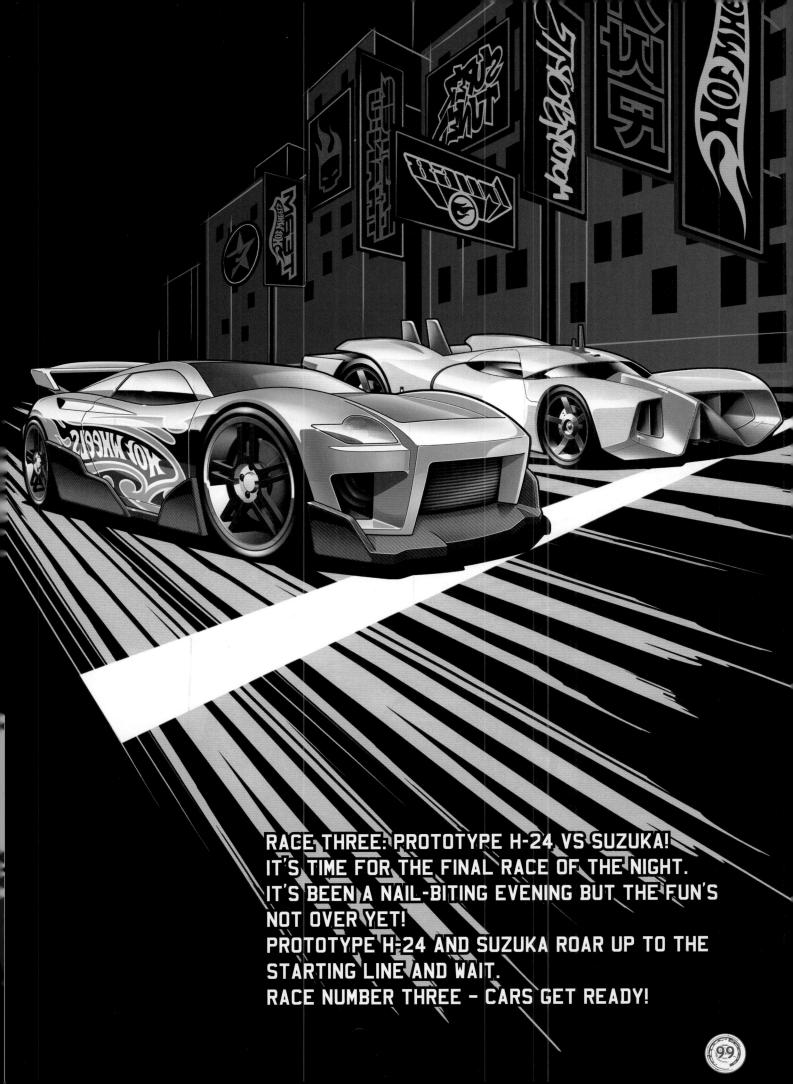

RACE THREE: PROTOTYPE H-24 VS SUZUKA!
IT'S TIME FOR THE FINAL RACE OF THE NIGHT.
IT'S BEEN A NAIL-BITING EVENING BUT THE FUN'S
NOT OVER YET!
PROTOTYPE H-24 AND SUZUKA ROAR UP TO THE
STARTING LINE AND WAIT.
RACE NUMBER THREE – CARS GET READY!

THE STARTER'S HORN BLASTS THREE TIMES AND THE CARS ZOOM OFF DOWN THE STREET.
THIS IS GOING TO BE THE TIGHTEST RACE OF THE NIGHT. THE TWO CARS ARE EQUALLY MATCHED. THE DRIVERS QUICKLY CHANGE GEAR WITHOUT LOSING ANY SPEED.

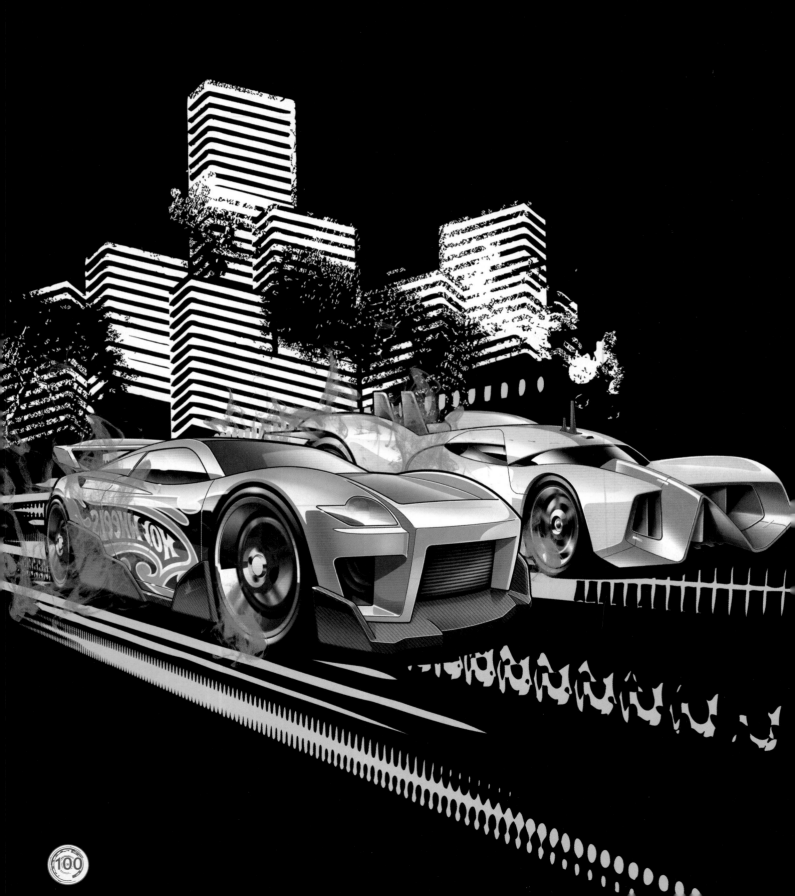

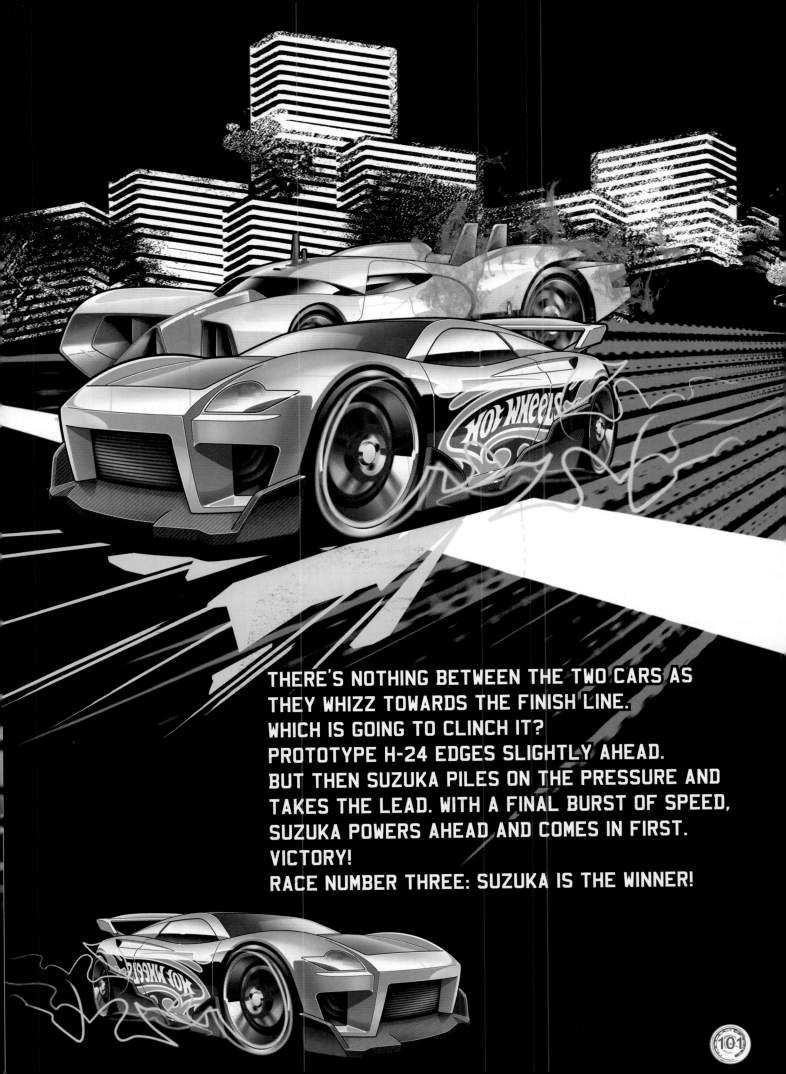

THERE'S NOTHING BETWEEN THE TWO CARS AS
THEY WHIZZ TOWARDS THE FINISH LINE.
WHICH IS GOING TO CLINCH IT?
PROTOTYPE H-24 EDGES SLIGHTLY AHEAD.
BUT THEN SUZUKA PILES ON THE PRESSURE AND
TAKES THE LEAD. WITH A FINAL BURST OF SPEED,
SUZUKA POWERS AHEAD AND COMES IN FIRST.
VICTORY!
RACE NUMBER THREE: SUZUKA IS THE WINNER!

CAR PARTS WORDSEARCH

LOOK AT THIS WORDSEARCH SQUARE AND SEE IF YOU CAN FIND ALL THESE HIDDEN CAR PARTS. THE WORDS READ ACROSS, DOWN, BACKWARDS AND FORWARDS – BUT ONE OF THE WORDS IS MISSING. WHEN YOU KNOW WHICH IT IS, WRITE THE WORD IN THE SPACE BELOW.

R	O	T	A	R	E	L	E	C	C	A	L	S	M	B
W	E	E	F	I	L	D	G	J	L	V	W	T	Z	V
X	L	I	S	D	E	H	O	R	N	W	Y	E	X	D
W	N	M	U	U	D	A	M	P	O	P	A	E	W	O
Z	E	C	N	O	F	N	D	N	O	W	A	R	D	O
W	E	I	R	Y	P	D	J	R	N	K	H	I	R	R
K	R	V	O	K	O	B	C	O	R	W	E	N	Y	C
L	C	A	O	O	Q	R	W	H	W	R	L	G	U	O
L	S	N	F	O	S	A	K	W	O	W	P	W	O	V
O	D	M	W	K	T	K	C	Z	Q	L	I	H	W	Q
I	N	W	E	W	U	E	I	L	W	G	O	E	D	R
T	I	N	D	I	C	A	T	O	R	O	U	E	I	J
A	W	E	E	R	A	J	S	E	E	H	J	L	O	O
R	T	W	P	E	T	R	O	L	C	A	P	K	B	T
B	R	A	K	E	S	W	U	I	L	S	E	R	Y	T

ACCELERATOR ☑   PETROL CAP ☑
BRAKES ☑   STEERING WHEEL ☑
DOOR ☑   SUNROOF ☑
HANDBRAKE ☑   TYRES ☐
HORN ☑   WINDSCREEN ☐

THE MISSING WORD IS: Indicator

102

TUNE-UP
JET THREAT

JET THREAT HAS COME TO THE GARAGE FOR A RE-SPRAY AND AN ENGINE TUNE-UP. THE MECHANIC IS JUST ABOUT TO GET TO WORK, BUT WHAT KIND OF TOOL IS HE USING? COLOUR IN THE SECTIONS MARKED WITH A DOT TO FIND OUT.

PICTURE YOUR DREAM RIDE!

A PHOTOGRAPHER IS OUT ON THE STREETS, TAKING PICTURES OF THE HOT WHEELS MACHINES. BUT THE CARS ARE SPEEDING PAST HIM SO QUICKLY HE'S ONLY MANAGED TO CAPTURE SMALL PIECES OF THEM! CAN YOU IDENTIFY THE CARS HE'S SNAPPED?

1. WHO AM I ?

2. WHO AM I ?

3. WHO AM I ?

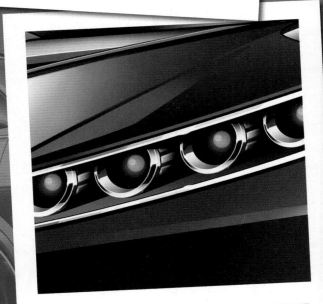

4. WHO AM I ?

5. WHO AM I ?

6. WHO AM I ?

THE CARS HE S SNAPPED ARE:

5000 FAST

MERCY BREAKER

CIRCLE TRACKER

JET THREAT

DRAGSTER

ULTRA RAGE

CAR COLLAGE!

NITRO DOORSLAMMER IS ONE INTENSE RIDE! YOU CAN MAKE THIS PICTURE OF NITRO DOORSLAMMER INTO A GREAT COLLAGE. FLICK THROUGH SOME COMICS OR MAGAZINES TO FIND THE COLOURS YOU WANT AND CUT THE PAGES INTO SMALL PIECES. YOU COULD ALSO USE SWEET WRAPPERS, TIN FOIL, COLOURED PAPER, TISSUE OR SCRAPS OF MATERIAL. STICK THE PIECES OVER NITRO DOORSLAMMER. IF YOU DON'T WANT TO USE THIS PAGE, ASK AN ADULT TO PHOTOCOPY IT FOR YOU FIRST.

ANSWERS...

P10 & 11 BURNIN' RUBBER
1. 5
2. HOT WHEELS WINTER RACE
3. RED
4. HARDDRIVE
5. 12
6. 7

P12 PARADIGM SHIFT PICK UP

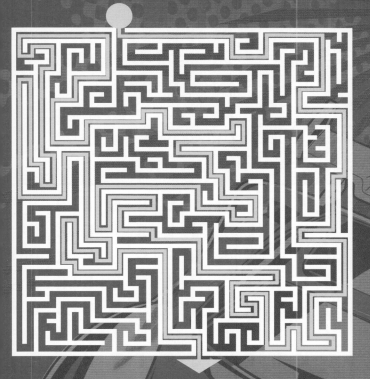

P13 MISSING HOT WHEELS
THE MISSING CAR IS SUZUKA

P14 & 15 SPEEDY SHADOWS
1. SPINE BUSTER
2. BONE SHAKER
3. BASSLINE
4. ROCKET BOX
5. NITRO DOORSLAMMER
6. DRAGSTER

P16 & 17 HOT WHEELS QUIZ
1. A
2. B
3. A
4. A
5. C
6. B
7. B
8. C
9. A
10. C

P21 MIXED UP MOTORS
1. RIVITED
2. HOLLOWBACK
3. RODGER DODGER
4. JACK HAMMER
5. BASSLINE
6. ROCKET BOX

P34 SCORCHING HOT DOT-TO-DOT!
A GAS (PETROL) STATION.

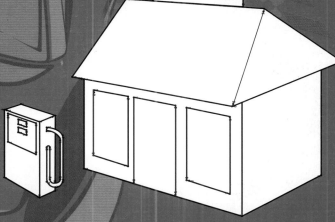

P35 RACING ROCKET FIRE
TRACK NUMBER 2

ANSWERS...

P36 & 37 JUMP INTO THE DRIVER'S SEAT

P39 WHICH IS THE REAL FAST FISH?
NUMBER 4

P40 MAGNIFICENT MECHANICS

THERE ARE 15 HIDDEN TYRES.

P43 CRAZY CAR CROSS WORD

HIDDEN WORD: HARDDRIVE

	W	H	E	E	L	S			
	C	A	R						
S	T	E	E	R	I	N	G		
		D	O	O	R				
I	N	D	I	C	A	T	O	R	
	B	R	A	K	E	S			
		I	G	N	I	T	I	O	N
	D	R	I	V	E	R			
P	U	N	C	T	U	R	E		

P58 PETROL STOP
PATH NUMBER 3

P59 HUNT THE HOT WHEELS

H	A	Y	E	N	I	L	S	S	A	B	N
A	H	O	L	L	O	W	B	A	C	K	O
R	W	A	V	N	B	F	G	J	W	X	U
D	E	W	I	S	W	A	D	F	S	O	M
D	R	E	K	A	H	S	E	N	O	B	Q
R	W	R	B	C	G	T	W	A	N	T	R
I	K	R	E	W	Q	F	I	T	K	E	S
V	D	E	T	I	V	I	R	F	D	K	Y
E	W	D	R	A	G	S	T	E	R	C	I
X	E	P	U	R	L	H	K	J	T	O	P
S	P	I	N	E	B	U	S	T	E	R	Z
V	B	N	W	T	W	I	N	M	I	L	L

P60 SPOT THE FAKE

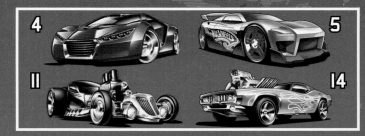

4   5

II   14

P61 WORD MATCH HOT WHEELS

S000 FAST
FAST FISH
RODGER DODGER
ULTRA RAGE
BONE SHAKER
JACK HAMMER
COOL ONE
CIRCLE TRACKER

P88 & 89 HOT WHEELS IN THE CITY

P64 MATCH 24/SEVEN

ODD ONE OUT

P102 CAR PARTS WORD SEARCH

R	O	T	A	R	E	L	E	C	C	A	L	S	M	B
W	E	E	F	I	L	D	G	J	L	V	W	T	Z	V
X	L	I	S	D	E	H	O	R	N	W	Y	E	X	D
W	N	M	U	U	D	A	M	P	O	P	A	E	W	O
Z	E	C	N	O	F	N	D	N	O	W	A	R	D	O
W	E	I	R	Y	P	D	J	R	N	K	H	I	R	R
K	R	V	O	K	O	B	C	O	R	W	E	N	Y	C
L	C	A	O	O	Q	R	W	H	W	R	L	G	U	O
L	S	N	F	O	S	A	K	W	O	W	P	W	O	V
O	D	M	W	K	T	K	C	Z	Q	L	I	H	W	Q
I	N	W	E	W	U	E	I	L	W	G	O	E	D	R
T	I	N	D	I	C	A	T	O	R	O	U	E	I	J
A	W	E	E	R	A	J	S	E	E	H	J	L	O	O
R	T	W	P	E	T	R	O	L	C	A	P	K	B	T
B	R	A	K	E	S	W	U	I	L	S	E	R	Y	T

THE MISSING WORD IS: INDICATOR

P66 & 67 S000 FAST VS ZOTIC MAZE

P104 & 105 PICTURE YOUR DREAM RIDE

1. DRAGSTER
2. CIRCLE TRACKER
3. S000 FAST
4. ULTRA RAGE
5. JET THREAT
6. MERCY BREAKER